THE INDUSTRIAL ARCHAEOLOGY
OF STAFFORDSHIRE

THE INDUSTRIAL ARCHAEOLOGY
OF THE BRITISH ISLES

Series Editor: E. R. R. GREEN

Cornwall, by A. C. Todd and Peter Laws
Derbyshire, by Frank Nixon
The East Midlands, by David M. Smith
Galloway, by Ian Donnachie
Hertfordshire, by W. Branch Johnson
Isle of Man, by T. A. Bawden, L. S. Garrad,
J. K. Qualtrough and J. W. Scatchard
The Lake Counties, by J. D. Marshall and M. Davies-Shiel
Lancashire, by Owen Ashmore
North-East England, by Frank Atkinson
Peak District, by Helen Harris
Scotland, by John Butt
Southern England (second edition, revised), by Kenneth Hudson
Staffordshire, by Robert Sherlock
Wales, by D. Morgan Rees

ASSOCIATED VOLUMES
The Bristol Region, by R. A. Buchanan and Neil Cossons
Dartmoor, by Helen Harris
Gloucestershire Woollen Mills, by Jennifer Tann
Stone Blocks and Iron Rails, by Bertram Baxter
The Tamar Valley (third impression, revised), by Frank Booker
Techniques of Industrial Archaeology, by J. P. M. Pannell
(second edition, revised by J. Kenneth Major)

OTHER INDUSTRIAL HISTORY
Brindley at Wet Earth Colliery, by A. G. Banks and R. B. Schofield
Bristol Brass, by Joan Day
The British Iron and Steel Industry, by W. K. V. Gale
The Early Factory Masters, by Stanley D. Chapman
The Engineering Industry of the North of Ireland, by W. E. Coe
A History of the Scottish Coal Industry, Vol. I 1700–1815,
by Baron F. Duckham
The History of Water Power in Ulster, by H. D. Gribbon

All these books are in uniform format

The Industrial Archaeology of
STAFFORDSHIRE

ROBERT SHERLOCK

DAVID & CHARLES
NEWTON ABBOT   LONDON
NORTH POMFRET (VT) VANCOUVER

ISBN 0 7153 5945 2

Library of Congress Catalog Card Number 74–20456

Set in 11 on 13pt Imprint and printed in Great
Britain by Latimer Trend & Company Ltd
Plymouth for David & Charles (Holdings)
Limited   South Devon House   Newton Abbot
Devon

Published in the United States of America
by David & Charles Inc   North Pomfret
Vermont 05053 USA

Published in Canada by Douglas David &
Charles Limited   3645 McKechnie Drive
West Vancouver BC

Contents

List of Illustrations

7

The plate of Boundary Works, Longton, is reproduced by courtesy of the National Monuments Record. All other plates are from photographs in the collection of the County Planning and Development Department, Stafford

DIAGRAMS IN TEXT

Preface

In 1956 Staffordshire County Council, in their role as local planning authority, decided to undertake a survey of the county's archaeological resources. Four years later the Council for British Archaeology, having recognised the value of industrial monuments and the seriousness of the threat affecting them, invited the County Council to undertake a pilot survey that would further the formulation of a national policy. This book is an indirect result of the acceptance of that invitation. It has therefore been very much a County Council project, and first acknowledgements are to the special sub-committee of the Town and Country Planning Committee who agreed to the writing of the book as an official duty by a member of the planning department staff. This unusual arrangement has been in keeping with a long-standing sense of responsibility towards archaeological interests.

The County Council's participation has been complemented by the help generously extended by so many private organisations and individuals. Owners have allowed access to their properties, in addition to which they have often been extremely informative. The coverage of certain subjects owes much to the generosity with which experts have shared their knowledge; they include Mr D. W. Crossley, Mr P. Guest, Mr W. E. C. Stuart, Lt-Colonel R. S. Williams-Thomas (glass); Mr T. R. Copeland, Mr A. R. Mountford, Mr M. I. Nixon (pottery); Mr M. A. Mosesson (leather); Mr T. L. Coxon, Mr W. Holt, Mr R. A. Lewis, Mr F. Peel (textiles); Mr B. G. Ward, Professor P. Mathias (malting and brewing); Mr F. A. Barnett, Mr A. J. R. Hickling (coal and iron); Dr J. A. Robey (copper); Mr J. R. Musgrave (roads); Mr. K. F. Gracie, Mr A. W. Jeffery (canals); Mr G. Biddle, Dr J. R. Hollick (railways); and Mr

11

J. A. Bedington, Mr C. Howell, Mr R. Wailes (watermills). Working together in Staffordshire has enabled stimulating exchanges with Mr M. W. Greenslade and Mr D. A. Johnson of the Staffordshire Victoria County History staff and with Mr F. B. Stitt, who as County Archivist and William Salt Librarian, looks after one of the finest aids to local history research in the provinces. Among colleagues, Mr J. H. Barratt, County Planning and Development Officer, Mr P. J. D. Goode, Principal Assistant Planning Officer, and Mrs P. M. Gray are deserving of special thanks. Mr G. R. Linecar provided the information for Fig, p 96. Mr G. N. Proud drew the figures except pp 28 and 38 which are by Mr R. B. Hardman, p 40 by Mrs C. Finlow, and pp 56, 62, 122 by Mr A. F. M. Jones. Mrs A. E. Ramsay and Mrs P. Brewer typed and retyped and retyped. Finally, because parts of the book were written at home, I thank my wife and family for uncommunicative evenings and weekends accepted with understanding and forbearance.

PART ONE

CHAPTER ONE

Diversity and Prosperity

WHEN in 1811 Staffordshire products were toasted with the words 'Crocks and Locks: and may we always have something to fill the one and guard with the other', the diversity of the county's industries was being acknowledged. Uniformity is not a characteristic of Staffordshire. The predominance of a single authority for local government justifies the county council's motto 'The Knot Unites', but in many respects Staffordshire is an area of divisions. Herein lies its interest and appeal, not least for the industrial archaeologist. As English counties go, Staffordshire is not particularly large. Only eighteenth in size before local government reorganisation, it measures 55 miles from north to south, and 36 miles from west to east. Yet those same miles take one across that ill-defined barrier between the Midlands and the North of England, and from the edge of the East Midlands into the heart of the West Midlands. Staffordshire is a border county, looking outwards to Manchester in the north and to Birmingham in the south, and the rainwater that falls near Maer can enter the River Trent, the River Severn or the River Mersey. Whichever direction it takes the water will have a long way to go before it reaches the open sea, for Staffordshire is about as far inland as any county can be, and not surprisingly it contains scarcely any length of navigable river. Without the cheap and easy carriage that water transport can provide Staffordshire was at a severe disadvantage compared with Lancashire and the North East, and it was not until the eighteenth century that the deficiencies of nature were remedied by artificial means. The construction of canals had a cataclysmic effect. Almost overnight Staffordshire found itself not only geographically but also economically at the centre of England; the dramatic overtones of the phrase Industrial Revolution have for Staffordshire some precision.

The potential that was waiting to be developed was the wealth of minerals. Copper and lead were available in the moorlands of the north-east; limestone was quarried primarily at Caldon Low and Dudley; sandstone for building purposes came from Gornal, Tixall and above all Hollington; gypsum had not only a value in itself but produced at Burton-upon-Trent a water that was pre-eminently suitable for brewing. The importance of the clay is sufficiently proclaimed by the existence of 'The Potteries' and by the prevalence of brick as a building material; fireclay around Stourbridge provided one of the basic requirements of the glass manufacturer; and salt was obtained by the evaporation of brine at Shirleywich and Weston, near Stafford. These minerals often had to be fired to be fully exploited. At first the firing was done with charcoal derived from the Staffordshire woodlands of Cannock Chase and Needwood Forest, but as the supplies of timber became exhausted increased attention was given to coal, the fuel that takes pride of place among Staffordshire minerals. Not only were the exposed coalfields extensive, but they had special qualities illustrated by the Ten Yard Seam of the Black Country, unrivalled in Great Britain for its combination of thickness and accessibility. Nor was this all, for the coal measures also yielded ironstone, and the exploitation of iron was a vital contributor to technological progress.

It was not until about 1766 that advantage was taken of the juxtaposition of iron and coal. John Wilkinson set up a steam-powered blast furnace. Before this, steam engines had been used for pumping, but for all other work the only sources of superhuman power were the horse and wind and water. The two latter sources were dependent upon geographical conditions, and one of the most significant factors that determined the history of the South Staffordshire coal and iron industry was the dearth of streams on the flat plateau that was eventually to be called the Black Country. The iron ore had to be carried off the plateau to where water power could be found to operate the bellows of the furnace and the tilt-hammer of the forge. Admittedly the iron industry was the most extravagant user of water,

Page 17 *Industrial archaeological earthworks:* (above) *Whiston inclined plane, Kingsley;* (below) *Ecton copper mines, Wetton*

Page 18 *The eighteenth-century Cheddleton flint mill. Maintained by Cheddleton Flint Mill Industrial Heritage Trust*

but there was also copper rolling, flint- and colour-grinding, cotton spinning and paper pulping, not to mention corn grinding which is common to every county but increased in importance as the number of mouths to feed increased. The compensation for an inland location was the presence of fast flowing streams. In the south, flowing conveniently off the Black Country, is the Stour, but most of Staffordshire drains into the Trent or its tributaries, the Sow, the Tame and the Dove. Yet the rivers by themselves were not enough, and windmills were a common ingredient of the Staffordshire scene. On a map of 1820 over fifty are shown. Some occupied conventional sites on isolated hilltops, but accessibility and nearness to a market could be more pressing considerations. The highest concentration of windmills was surprisingly in the Black Country, and many of the later examples were located near the newly built canals.

Although the nature of Staffordshire's resources, geographical and geological, favoured industry, the human element also played its part. The county was fortunate in its association with some of the great names of the Industrial Revolution. James Brindley spent part of his early life at Leek and did much of his canal building in Staffordshire. Robert Peel, father of the prime minister, made his home at Drayton Bassett and the centre of his cotton-spinning interests at Tamworth and Fazeley. Worthington, Bass, Allsopp and Wilson are among the dynasties of Burton brewers. In the Potteries, Josiah Spode, Thomas Minton and Josiah Wedgwood contributed to the reputation of Staffordshire earthenware and porcelain while Wedgwood had the added distinction of promoting the improvement of the roads and the construction of canals. In the south, the most memorable figure was perhaps the already mentioned John Wilkinson, 'father of the South Staffordshire iron industry', who co-operated with Boulton & Watt in the boring of steam-engine cylinders, who used raw coal rather than charcoal in his furnaces, and who introduced the steam-driven hammer. Boulton & Watt's factory is sited in what is now part of Birmingham, but during the whole of its active life it lay within Staffordshire.

B

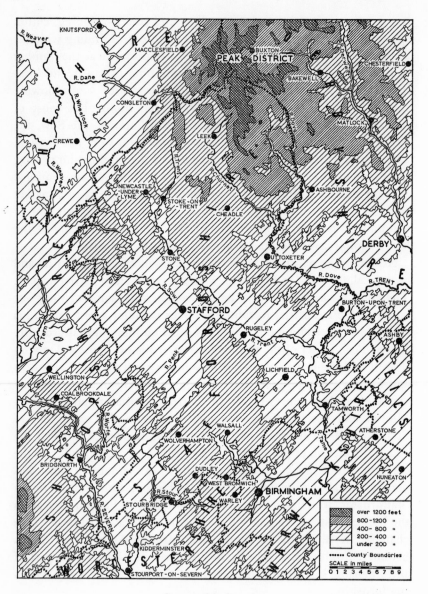

Geographical setting

Human inventiveness was essential, but to an increasing extent progress and successful exploitation of resources depended on the availability of capital. In the nineteenth century some of the capitalists were men like John Robinson McClean whose wealth was derived from prudent application of technical ability, but even in that century and certainly earlier the aristocratic landowners were the chief investors. The Marquis of Stafford, the Marquis of Anglesey, Earl Talbot, Lord Ward, the Duke of Sutherland, the Earl of Dartmouth and the Duke of Devonshire were all owners of valuable mines for coal and other minerals, and their seats, as at Trentham, Himley and Sandwell, were sometimes so close to the centres of industry as to be deserted by the families who built them.

The influence of the great landowners also made itself felt in the country. Because of the intensive development of the Potteries on the one hand and of the Black Country on the other it is easy to forget that Staffordshire is predominantly a rural county and that agriculture and the use of a by-product of stockbreeding, leather, are and long have been principal industries. The agents of the landed estates were as keen to improve the efficiency of the farms and mills as that of the coalmines, and the most advanced agricultural buildings tend to be those that reflect the benefit of ample capital resources and a willingness to pioneer. Layouts were re-designed so as to reduce handling and carriage and to make maximum use of power.

Equally it was the wealthy industrial owners who could afford architectural embellishments. Much of the Staffordshire metal-working industry was organised by factors and the contracts were undertaken in back-yard workshops. In such circumstances there was the very opposite of any architectural pretentiousness. At iron-foundries and collieries the scale could be different, but here also there was no direct point of contact with the public consumer, and the incentive to make buildings attractive as well as functional scarcely arose. The vertical engine-houses at Stafford Colliery, Fenton, now demolished, were an exception proving the rule, for this was a colliery partly owned by the Duke of Sutherland, and

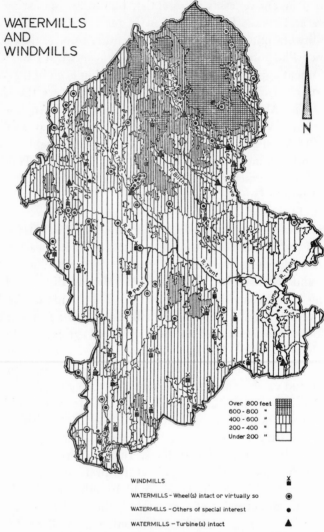

WATERMILLS
AND
WINDMILLS

N

Over 800 feet
600 - 800 "
400 - 600 "
200 - 400 "
Under 200 "

WINDMILLS   ✕

WATERMILLS – Wheel(s) intact or virtually so   ◉

WATERMILLS – Others of special interest   ●

WATERMILLS – Turbine(s) intact   ▲

Watermills and windmills. Based on survey 1966–9

moreover the depth of the pits deserved some special acknowledgement. The textile manufacturers were more concerned with their public image, and in any case they or the managers often had to live beside the source of livelihood. The repetitive arrangement both of the bays and of the floors moreover invited an orderly architectural treatment. Where the mill faced a public road there might even be an inducement to relieve the monotony of the brickwork and to emphasise the symmetry with a central pediment and cupola; thereupon the mill assumed the guise adopted for so many industrial buildings of the eighteenth and nineteenth centuries. The same treatment was found to be suitable for a pottery so long as the ovens could be screened behind the frontage and so long as a carriage entrance gave access to the yard.

Even if some of the industrial buildings are pretentious, there is little evidence in Staffordshire of the employment of professional architects. This may be because the records have not been studied enough, or because the relevant ones have largely disappeared. The results would suggest that the jobs of builder and architect were combined, and indeed the division between the two occupations was still obscure in the nineteenth century when architects like Henry Ward of Hanley and his namesake of Stafford could both begin their careers as builders. When an architect was engaged, a local man would almost certainly be chosen: the kind of person who would otherwise be designing cheap churches, Noncomformist chapels and middle-class housing. It was only when the building was of a special type that recourse was had to architects from farther afield. The classic example is the station, whether of the kind associated with stationary engines or with locomotives. Many of the early railway stations in Staffordshire were the work of London architects, and how the arts of engineering and architecture could be splendidly combined is illustrated by pumping stations at Sandfields (Lichfield), Hatton (Swynnerton) and Bratch (Wombourne).

Regardless of any architectural or other merit, the eighteenth- and nineteenth-century industrial monuments of Staffordshire are being destroyed at an increasing rate. Josiah Wedgwood's pottery at Etruria has gone, while single-storey factories and housing estates have transformed the face of the Black Country. Leek is the only town still dominated by its early industrial buildings. Ironically the finest Staffordshire monuments are now to be found in the villages and in the country where pressures to demolish and to redevelop have been less acute than in the towns. Some of the cotton mills fall within this category, as do the pumping stations, which although designed to serve the conurbations, had to be away from them and where the water was. Steam power is now almost a nostalgic memory, the fires of the last coal-fired pottery kiln went out in 1970, and new materials and new methods of manufacture are affecting the textile mills. The extent of both the canal and railway systems has been curtailed, and in 1971 the National Coal Board operated only twelve deep mines within the county. But despite all the destruction and change, industrial monuments have survived. Some are derelict; others are mutilated and disfigured by advertisements; others thanks to enlightened owners are carefully preserved. Enough remains on the ground to bear witness to the achievements that in any case show themselves in the prosperity of twentieth-century Staffordshire. The toast that there may be crocks and locks and something to fill the one and be guarded with the other is still fulfilled.

CHAPTER TWO

Glass, Pottery, and Leather

GLASS

IT is somewhat ironic that Staffordshire should produce from two of its less conventionally attractive areas two of its most self-consciously beautiful products. The same coal that sullied the landscape and created conditions where living standards were sacrificed to the quick acquisition of wealth, heated the furnaces and kilns of the potter and glassmaker. There was, however, a time when glassmaking was essentially a rural industry, and it did not finally cease to be so until the royal proclamation of 1615, forbidding the burning of wood in furnaces. The interest of the Staffordshire glassworking sites is that they provide an opportunity to study both the rural and urban phases of the industry.

The earlier phase is associated especially with Bagot's Park near Abbots Bromley and with Bishop's Wood near Eccleshall. In 1965 land reclamation at Bagot's Park resulted in the surface discovery of fragments of glass and of glazed crucibles. The fragments were concentrated at fifteen different sites, evenly distributed, and in 1966 an excavation of one of these sites was undertaken by Mr D. W. Crossley. The structure most readily identifiable proved to be the furnace in which the glass underwent its main melting. The heat, about 1,200° C, was provided by two fires, burning scrub-wood, at opposite ends of a central flue, and the flames from the fires entered the furnace through arches and met under a reverberatory clay dome. Over the whole structure was a tile-covered roof, supported by 15in posts at the four corners. It is not known how the crucibles placed on platforms flanking the flue were moved into position, but the discovery of a working-hole cover indicates the means whereby the craftsman could thrust his gathering-iron through the roof of the

25

furnace and take molten glass from the adjacent crucible. The product of the site was Crown window glass, and the date of operation seems to have been the early sixteenth century. The pottery finds indicated this date, and so also did the magnetic orientation assumed by the clay and brick at the time of the last firing.

The date of the Bagot's Park furnace is of great importance for, if it is early sixteenth century, it belongs to a time when glassmaking in Staffordshire was still, so far as can be judged, a native tradition. Place-names, personal names and other documentary evidence testify to the presence of glassmakers in Staffordshire from at least 1289 onwards and to their special connection with Abbots Bromley and Wolseley near Rugeley. But until the discoveries at Bagot's Park were made the achievements of these early glassworkers had tended to be discounted.

The reason for such treatment lies in the emphasis that has been placed on the arrival of immigrants—the Tyzacks, the Henzeys and the Titterys—from Lorraine. They settled about 1567 in south-west Surrey, and by 1585 some had moved to Staffordshire. In that year one of them, Ambrose Henzey, entered into an agreement with Richard Bagot whereby the latter was to set up a glasshouse at Bagot's Park, and to provide fuel and lodgings for the workmen. The former was to pay Bagot and to provide his own ashes and clay. No glass-working site at Bagot's Park has yet been associated with Ambrose Henzey but in Bishop's Wood a furnace has been excavated and, because of the presence of Tyzacks and Henzeys in Eccleshall parish between 1585 and 1604, it is reasonable to attribute this to the glassmakers from Lorraine. Whereas nothing visible now remains at Bagot's Park, it fortunately proved possible at Bishop's Wood to preserve and partially to reconstruct the glass furnace so that the general principles of operation can be understood. Despite its later date and despite the supposed influence from Lorraine, the Bishop's Wood furnace does not differ so noticeably from that at Bagot's Park. The former was, however, more substantial, and the superstructure was at least partly of stone rather than entirely of clay.

The consumption of wood by the early glassmakers reached alarming proportions, and it has been calculated that about 4 acres of fifteen-year-old coppice would need to be cleared each month for the use of a single furnace. Supplies of timber were near enough to becoming exhausted to explain why, even before the royal proclamation, Lorraine glassmakers had moved to the Kingswinford–Stourbridge area, attracted by the plentiful supply of coal for the furnaces and of fireclay for the pots or crucibles. Paul Tyzack, who had previously been at Eccleshall, was in Kingswinford parish by 1612, and it would have been partly the success of the glassmakers at Kingswinford that established the practicability of using coal and helped to justify the prohibition of the use of timber.

In 1621 two of the four glasshouses in England were at Stourbridge, which is striking evidence of the area's immediate importance. There are no surviving seventeenth-century buildings associated with the Stourbridge glass industry, and it has been suggested that it was not until about 1750 that the glass-cone, giving individuality to the urban scene, began to make its appearance. The cone was the logical development of the kind of building represented at Bagot's Park but, instead of an over-all roof, both protection from the weather and disposal of waste gases resulted at one and the same time from the simple expedient of an outer cover that was also a chimney. In the centre there still remained the series of pots, but now the arrangement was circular rather than rectangular. There could be as many as ten or twelve pots, with a corresponding number of glassworking teams; the flames entered the furnace through a central eye, and beneath was the 'cave' where radiating tunnels led to the fire and provided not only a draught but also a means of delivering coal and extracting ashes. Pots could be replaced by breaking open the fireclay fillings to the arches that supported the furnace dome, and the provision for draught was increased by openings round the circumference of the cone.

The main purpose of the cone was thus fulfilled, but almost as important were the subsidiary processes. There had to be separate

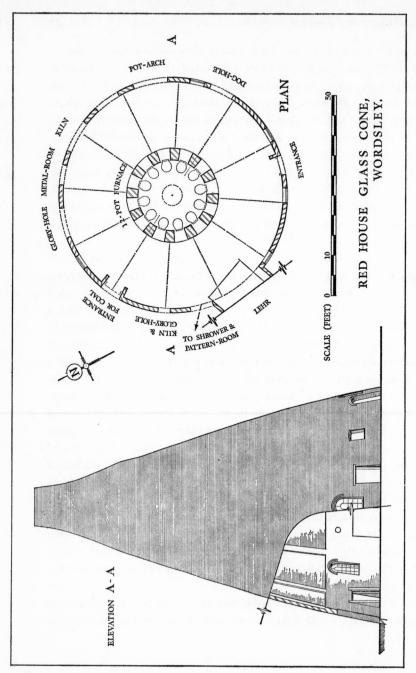

A

POT-ARCH

DOG-HOLE

KILN

GLORY-HOLE METAL-ROOM

17-POT FURNACE

ENTRANCE

ENTRANCE
FOR COAL

KILN &
GLORY-HOLE

LEHR

TO SHROWER &
PATTERN-ROOM

A

PLAN

N

SCALE (FEET)   0   10   50

RED HOUSE GLASS CONE,
WORDSLEY.

ELEVATION A - A

Red House glass-cone, Wordsley, Dudley

furnaces for pre-heating the pots in the pot-arch and for re-heating the glass during working. In addition there was the kiln for annealing. A cone was therefore a highly complex structure, and yet the heating and blowing of the glass was only part of the activities of a glassworks. The silica, lead oxide and potash had to be mixed, vessels might have to be cut and engraved, and there was also the problem of packing and storage. By the time a steam engine and offices had been included, a nineteenth-century glassworks could cover an acre.

At the time of the Tithe Survey, about 1840, there were six glassworks in the parish of Kingswinford. With one exception they were all adjacent to a canal. Only the two separate works on either side of High Street, Wordsley (Dudley), now united under the ownership of Stuart & Sons Ltd, are still flourishing. The other manufacturers of hand-blown glass remaining in the Stourbridge area are Webb Corbett Ltd, and Stevens & Williams Ltd. The former who are just over the border into Worcestershire also have the works at Tutbury; the latter moved to their present site in Moor Lane, Brierley Hill, in 1870, but can trace their history back to about 1760.

Generally it has been possible to retain and adapt the eighteenth- and nineteenth-century brick buildings. The three Staffordshire glass-cones that survive are all used for storage. The Dial cone at Audnam (Dudley) was truncated in 1936. Of the two belonging to Stuart & Sons Ltd at Wordsley one was truncated in 1939; the other is intact and one of the outstanding industrial monuments of the Black Country. Although gas and electric firing have revolutionised the design of the glassworks, nevertheless the methods of making handmade glass have changed little since the days of the construction of cones or even before. The blowing and shaping of the glass allows little scope for mechanisation.

POTTERY

The other ornamental product of Staffordshire is its pottery, and there are a number of characteristics possessed in common by pottery and glass. To the advantage of the excavating archaeologist, both are sensitive to changes in taste and both are easily broken. Glass has to be cooled where pottery has to be heated, but even so the working of the two materials is not altogether dissimilar, and a glassworks and a pottery share a superficial resemblance. The equivalent of the glass-cone is the bottle oven, and because potting likewise involves a series of different processes there is a corresponding multiplicity of work-shops, communicating with one another by means of a central yard. To facilitate the movement of the goods as each process is completed, buildings are not normally more than two storeys high. Both the glassworks and the pottery consumed large quantities of coal so that nearness to the coalfield was important, especially as the same coal-field could supply the fireclay not only for the crucibles and the saggars but also for the linings of the furnaces and the ovens. The two industries therefore to some extent depended on the same raw materials, but their distribution in Staffordshire is now markedly separate. Pottery is the industry of the north of the county.

The Potteries centred on Stoke-on-Trent is a phenomenon unique in Britain. Nowhere else may be found an area so identified with one particular industry as to bear the name of that industry. The name was first applied in the mid-eighteenth century, and the need for it is in itself evidence of the previous anonymity. In the Middle Ages pottery was being made in North Staffordshire, but so was it also in countless other places. By the end of the seventeenth century, how-ever, Burslem-made pots of Uttoxeter-produced butter were reaching London and, thanks to the superior clays, Burslem was recognised as the greatest potting-town in the county.

During the first half of the eighteenth century the improvements in techniques and their growing sophistication led to the artisan assum-ing more and more the status of a specialist. No longer was potting a side-activity to be practised by the farmer in some rudimentary buildings adjoining his dwelling, even if farming might remain a supplementary source of income. But it was not until about 1750 that a large planned works was erected, and even then the traditional layout with the owner's house occupying the frontage persisted. The works of Thomas and John Wedgwood at Ivy House have gone, but the associated Big House remains.

The next stage in the process of evolution, the purpose-built factory, was dramatically reached in 1767 when Josiah Wedgwood started to build the Etruria factory and his house, Etruria Hall, a quarter of a mile away. It was the most important event in the industrial and architectural history of the Potteries. The works, down by the route of the Trent & Mersey Canal, established a tradition of design, influential enough to have been followed with little variation for over a hundred years. The house was now a separate entity, and a two-fold focus of attention was created first by the house and secondly by the offices, warehouses and those other parts of the pottery itself that could conveniently conform to a single architectural treatment. A potter might be concerned with his public image, and what the public saw at the Etruria factory and elsewhere was an essay in Palladianism—a large two- or three-storey façade with windows regularly spaced and a central entrance.

The clearly recognisable succession of manufacturing processes lead one to expect a corresponding order in the arrangement of the buildings and that the plans of potteries would to some extent resemble one another. But an inspection of the 1 : 500 Ordnance Survey maps for Longton, that resulted from a survey of 1856–7, show that this was far from being so. The identity of each part of each works is indicated, and the striking feature is the arbitrariness and dissimilarity of the plans. Samuel Scriven, when in 1841 he presented his report to the Children's Employment Commission, divided the Staffordshire potteries into three categories. First there were 'those of most recent structure; many of them built upon scales of great magnitude, in some instances of beauty'. They contained 'large, well ventilated, light, airy, commodious rooms, in all respects adapted to the nature of the processes carried on in them'. There were 25 potteries in this category. Secondly there were the 64 potteries where from 50 to 100 hands were employed. 'Most of them have been erected many years, and as the trade has increased, so the rooms appear to have increased in a corresponding ratio. Some here and there, upon, around and about the first premises, so that there is neither order, regularity, nor proportion; the consequence of this is, that men, women and children are to be passing in and out, to and fro, to their respective departments all hours of the day no matter what the weather, warm, cold, wet, or dry; the rooms, with very few exceptions, are either low, damp, close, small, dark, hot, dirty, ill ventilated, or unwholesome, or have all these disadvantages.' By the time that Scriven came to describe the thirty-eight potteries in the third category, his supply of adjectives was exhausted. If this were possible, they were even worse than the others.

The attitude to accommodation was summed up in 1841 by Thomas Shelley who worked in the office at Zachariah Boyle's factory in Stoke-on-Trent: 'The rooms are small and low; but you must take them as they were built.' This is what in fact most potters did. Few seem to have had the capital resources of the cotton manufacturer or the brewer to embark on large redevelopment schemes, and in any case there was always the risk on a cramped site of interrupting production. So the old unsuitable rooms remained. The situation would have been worsened by the frequent changes of ownership that characterise the history of so many of the Staffordshire potteries.

At the Etruria works there was the main yard behind the elaborate entrance façade. This was Big Yard where useful ware was made. To the north lay Black Bank Yard where basalt ware was manufactured. Production began and ended near the canal and basin so that this was where the clay stores, the crate sheds, and the coopers' shop and stores were sited. The Spode pottery in Stoke was another example of a large works. When visited by Charles Knight about 1849 it covered about 10 acres and gave employment to a maximum of nearly 1,000 hands. But even here expansion had been achieved at the expense of efficiency and Knight noted the 'great irregularity'. Two features repeated from the Etruria works did, however, betray some sense of order. One was the division of the works as indicated by the names of the yards: 'plate', 'saucer', 'dish', 'coloured body', 'printers', 'porcelain' and 'black'. The second was the storage of stone, flint, chert, gypsum, marl and clay in the large open area beside the canal. But a canal-side location was exceptional, and for most potteries the more important consideration was nearness to coal, water and tramways.

One of the factors that might have influenced the plan of potteries was alignment for the application of steam power. But such power was little used except for the preparation of materials, and in *The Potters' Examiner* of 3 August 1844 readers were informed that 'of all trades of this great manufacturing country, the potting trade has been the least injured by mechanical appliances'. This state of affairs was about to be threatened. The introduction of machinery that year for making patch-boxes at John Ridgway's works forewarned tender-hearted parents of the cries of hungry children 'when the hearth-stone is desolate, and the cupboard is empty'. It was evidently considered preferable to have these selfsame children providing the power, either as jiggers turning the jigger or horizontal wheel for the flat-ware maker, or as mould-runners carrying flat ware to the hot-house and returning with the moulds. In 1841 the statement 'We have no engine, having no occasion, as all the work is done by hand,' was true for all but the largest works, and this despite a long familiarisation with steam and other sources of power. Thomas Wedgwood had a horse gin as early as 1678, and Erasmus Darwin designed a windmill for Josiah Wedgwood at Etruria. The first steam engine to be used in a pottery was that acquired about 1779 by Josiah Spode. Three or four Boulton & Watt steam engines were supplied for the Etruria works between about 1782 and 1800, and Minton's in 1819 acquired a 24hp engine from Christopher Kirk. At Spode's pottery, the engines drove the throwing wheels and turning lathes, but elsewhere the function of these early engines seems to have been grinding, milling and mixing.

Ovens could be classified according to whether the flames were conducted upwards or downwards by the draught. The actual oven where the pots were placed had a firebrick floor, and it was heated by a series of fires round the circumference. Enclosing the oven was a brick outer casing, known as the hovel. The hovel, which increased the draught, could be separated from the oven, allowing the fires to be stoked in the space between them. Or the hovel and oven walls could be contiguous in which case the fires were stoked from outside. The flames entered at the bottom, and in an up-draught oven they escaped through holes in the roof. A down-draught oven, on the other hand, had no such holes. The flames were forced downwards by the domed roof, and they entered the hovel through holes in the floor and flues. In both types of oven cooling was hastened by removal of dampers in the roof. From the outside, up-draught and down-draught kilns are not necessarily distinguishable, but those with no space between the oven and hovel will have their overall shape determined by the vertical sides and domed roof of the oven.

The different shapes of the ovens are indeed a large part of their fascination; they are all basically bottle-shaped but there is every variation from the structure resembling a glass-cone to the slender stack with a swollen base. The building of a bottle-oven presented to the bricklayer the same kind of challenge as Brindley's canal bridges, and the variation is further increased by the situation. Some ovens were free-standing, but others, especially in Longton where congestion was acute, were surrounded by other buildings. The tops emerged from above the roofs like obese chimneys.

Although the potteries offered opportunities to the architectural profession it was a chance that was rarely taken. In Longton the premises of the Longton Pottery Co Ltd, Barker Street, and those on the west side of Landon Street illustrate the small works, centred round a yard and lacking all frills. On the opposite side of Landon Street, the Albert Works is on a larger scale and its High Street frontage is a single composition. Only occasionally was a whole pottery conceived architecturally. Enoch Wood's Fountain Place Works at Burslem adjoined a noble Georgian house, and a medieval flavour was imparted by the embattled tops to the boundary walls and ovens. Samuel Alcock

Page 35   *Steam power for water pumping:* (above) *Mill Meece, Eccleshall;*
(below) *Sandfields, Lichfield*

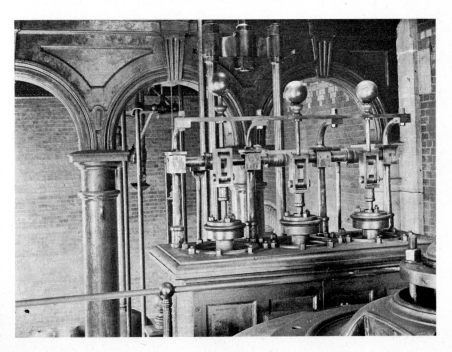

Page 36 *Functionalism and the public image:* (above) *ovens at Edensor Road, Longton:* (below) *Boundary Works, Longton, early nineteenth century*

employed Thomas Stanley, a Shelton architect, when the front of the Hill Pottery, Burslem, was built in 1839. William Boulton of Stafford designed an earthenware factory apparently at Longton in 1845; and Charles Lynam, the ecclesiastical architect, designed the new tile-works for Minton & Co at Stoke in 1868. But where it was merely proposed to screen a pottery behind a new façade, this would have lain within the competence of a builder, so long as he was equipped with one of the contemporary guides to Palladian architecture. Any sophistication was reserved for the entrance which was either at a corner, as at Wade Heath & Co Ltd's Burslem pottery, or at the centre, as at Boundary Works, Longton. The extremes of extravagance were reached at Hill Pottery, Burslem, where pairs of Ionic columns supported plinths and urns. The idioms were taken from the Palladian repertoire and included central projecting bays and an elliptically arched entrance, a tripartite arrangement of the windows, a keystone decorated with a device such as an urn, a pediment containing a clock-dial or an inscription tablet and, finally, on the roof, a cupola and bell. And what is most remarkable is the persistence of this tradition. John Aynsley's pottery at Sutherland Road, Longton, dates from 1861; yet it is strikingly similar to Josiah Wedgwood's pottery of nearly a hundred years before. The Gothic Revival seems to have been scarcely noticed.

The life of an oven was about twenty to thirty years, and ovens were still being built and rebuilt until comparatively recently. Those in Edensor Road, Longton, are representative. Two at Garfield works, also in Longton, bear the dates 1927 and 1939. But there was a very serious objection to the traditional form of kiln, and this was the intermittency of the firing. In a biscuit oven the wares had to be heated for forty or fifty hours, and then the oven had to be allowed to cool gradually. It was not until 1912 that the tunnel kiln, allowing a continuous process, was first introduced. At about the same time gas and electricity replaced coal and so enabled much greater control over temperature and atmosphere to be achieved. The disadvantage to the tunnel kiln was its length. Potteries had to be partly redesigned

c

DOWNDRAUGHT BISCUIT OVEN

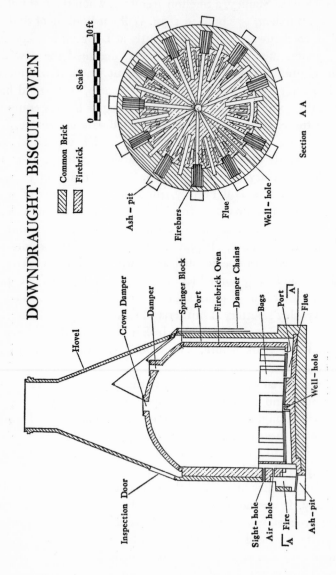

Pottery-firing oven. Based on drawing of typical design by M. I. Nixon, 1969

to accommodate it. Even so the adoption of tunnel kilns spread, and the most dramatic recent change in the potteries has been the disappearance and disuse of the coal-fired oven.

During the 1960s the factories that were demolished included May Place (Burslem), Hill Works (Burslem), Furnival's (Cobridge), Ridgway's (Burslem), Greenfield's (Tunstall) and most notably the Etruria works. Destruction has now reached a point where the desirability of selective preservation can be recognised. Spode Ltd at Stoke are to be congratulated on retaining and preserving the kiln of their last bottle oven. At Longton, there is the Gladstone Works in Uttoxeter Road which has changed little in its plan since 1857. Its most notable features are the three-storey street façade and the four main bottle ovens. The works has been obtained by a charitable trust which, with financial support from local businessmen and others, has the aim of restoring it as a working industrial museum.

Clearance preceding redevelopment has not been entirely to the disservice of the archaeologist. The Stoke-on-Trent Museum Archaeological Society has been showing the value of excavation. At Burslem the Hill Top site produced a remarkable collection of 82 slip-ware dishes, belying the notion that all the pottery of about 1700 was highly decorated while, nearby, on the site of Swan Bank Methodist Church, new evidence for the development of salt-glazing between 1680 and 1740 was obtained. No structures have been found at Burslem, but at the site of the Longton Hall porcelain works, excavations in conjunction with the British Museum uncovered the base foundations of three mid-eighteenth-century porcelain kilns. It is hoped to re-erect one of these bases, that of the glost kiln, at the City Museum & Art Gallery, Hanley.

Crate making

In the potteries, as in the glass industry, there was little of the intense specialisation that characterised, for instance, some of the metalworking industries. The master potter was, with few exceptions, responsible for everything from the receipt of the raw materials to the

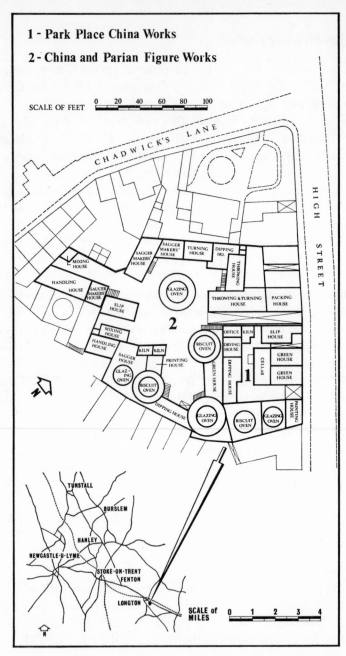

1 - Park Place China Works

2 - China and Parian Figure Works

SCALE OF FEET

Gladstone Works, Longton, Stoke-on-Trent. Based on copies
of Ordnance Survey maps, 1 : 500 (1857) at Staffordshire Record
Office, D593/H/8/98, Crown Copyright reserved

sale of the finished goods. One of the exceptions was the crate making, which could be carried on in a separate range of single-storey buildings. Mr Samuel Warren of Edensor Road, Longton, still makes crates for the pottery industry. The technique is to form a framework of sawn (formerly cleft) hardwood and then to interweave hazel through holes in the framework. The structure is finally secured with wedges. A distinctive feature of a crate maker's site are the chimneys, marking the positions of the wood-fired hearths over which the hazel is heated to make it pliable.

Paper making

A second instance of dependence on outside manufacturers is provided by paper making. The pottery industry has had an interest in paper since about 1785 when tissue paper began to be used in the transfer printing from designs on copper plates on to earthenware. One of the most important of the present paper-making firms is Brittains Ltd of Cheddleton. The existing works is almost entirely twentieth-century, but tissue paper has been made on the site since at least 1841 when a paper-making machine of the 'newest construction' was driven by a 4hp steam engine, and two rag machines were driven by a 16hp marine steam engine. The waterwheel had already been superseded by that date.

Grinding of raw materials

A third manufacture associated with the pottery industry was the grinding of materials. This seems to have been undertaken on the premises only by the largest firms. The materials to be ground numbered four: firstly, Cornish stone, generally used in the making of a porcelain body from 1775 and ground in Cornwall; secondly, colour; thirdly, calcined bone; fourthly, calcined flint which, by the late seventeenth century was known to improve the whiteness and vitrification of the body and to withstand firing better. The flints were at first ground dry, but the dust thereby created presented a hazard to health, and in 1726 and 1732 Thomas Benson of Newcastle-under-

Lyme took out patents for a process that enabled the flints to be ground in water.

Benson's process has been followed in principle ever since, although the only materials now ground are bone and colours. The flints were mainly derived from Gravesend and Sussex, and they were charged with alternate layers of coal in a brick-lined kiln. Having been calcined, the flints were usually crushed and were then ready for grinding which was effected in a circular pan, about 12ft diameter. The pavement of the pan corresponded to the bedstone of a corn-grinding mill and was of Flintshire chert so carefully laid as to present a perfectly smooth surface. The function of the runner stone was performed by blocks of Derbyshire chert, appropriately called 'runners', which were driven round by a varying number of arms attached to a central shaft. The flints were ground in water until the mixture reached a creamy consistency when it was run off into a wash tub and agitated by means of openwork wooden paddles. It was then run off into the settling ark where the correctly ground material could be recognised by the level at which it settled, and from here it was pumped to the kiln for the final process of drying.

The factor that at first determined the location of grinding mills was the availability of water which was required both for washing and to drive machinery. Since the transport of the raw materials and of the finished product was the other important consideration, most of the mills tended to be sited near either roads or canals that gave ready access to the Potteries. The three main concentrations were, first, along the River Churnet as far as Consall and Froghall (so as to be near the Caldon Branch of the Trent & Mersey Canal); secondly, along the River Trent as far as Hoo near Ingestre (so as to be near the main canal); and thirdly, along the Moddershall Valley through which the road from Stone to Longton ran. So suitable were the conditions in the Moddershall Valley that eight mills were clustered along a length of only 2 miles.

Some water-powered mills, such as Boothen and Foley, were in the Potteries or on their edge. It would have been desirable to have had

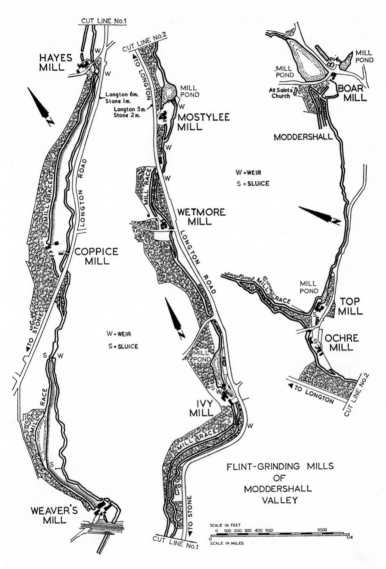

Flint-grinding mills, Moddershall Valley. Based on Ordnance
Survey maps, 1:2500 (1957–8), Crown Copyright reserved

more mills in this position; experiments were made with wind power but, in the end, convenience was increasingly achieved by the use of steam. In 1807 Robert Hamilton, earthenware manufacturer, was buying a 32hp engine from Boulton & Watt for his flint mill at Stoke. In 1829 a colour-mill at Shelton, driven by a 'newly-erected 5 h.p. steam-engine', was commended for its central situation. In 1844, the mill for grinding flint and potters' materials at Bridge Street, Stoke, was powered by a 24hp steam engine and belonged, as so many others did, to a firm of potters. Or there might be a combination of the two sources of power water and steam.

Despite the introduction of ball mills in 1910, a number of pan mills may be seen working. Water power is still used at Froghall for the grinding of colour, and one of the last remaining working steam engines was until 1972 the source of power at the Etruscan Bone & Flint Mill in the heart of the Potteries. At two of the mills in the Moddershall Valley, waterwheels were driving pans for grinding bone until 1965, and three of the other mills in this valley, although disused, retain substantial parts of their machinery. But perhaps the most impressive monument of all is the mill with its pair of wheels at Cheddleton. It has been restored to working order by a specially created preservation trust.

LEATHER

The preparation and working of leather was at first related to the rural parts of Staffordshire where livestock provided the hides and trees provided the bark for tanning. Stone commended itself in 1823 because 500 head of beef were slaughtered there annually, and in 1836 the woodlands of the Barlaston neighbourhood were said to afford a plentiful supply of oak bark for tanning. The skinyard or tanyard by a stream and on the outskirts of the town was a characteristic sight and smell, and the social status enjoyed by the tanner is still evidenced by two notable town houses, No 28 Eastgate Street, Stafford, and No 2 Lower High Street, Tutbury. At Rugeley the owner lived within the curtilage of a large tannery that incorporated a brick dated 1791 and stood beside both a stream and the Trent & Mersey Canal. Tanning presupposed some capital investment; the working of leather on the other hand long remained a domestic industry.

The three Staffordshire towns still particularly associated with leather-working are Walsall, Stafford and Stone. In the sixteenth century Walsall was already a centre of manufacture for saddlers' ironmongery, which must help to explain why leather-working gravitated towards that town in the first half of the nineteenth century. There is now little physical evidence of that development, since virtually all the tanneries have been demolished and there is almost nothing to distinguish the premises of the leatherworking trades from other nineteenth century industrial buildings. However, leatherworking remains an important social and commercial element in Walsall life.

Stafford and Stone were and are the centres of shoe-making, and at Stafford the changes resulting from the introduction of a factory system are more clearly seen. William Horton is thought to have established the first shoe factory there towards the end of the eighteenth century, but the main group of surviving factories belong to the second half of the nineteenth century. They are all in the north end of the town, concentrated in the triangle formed by Foregate Street, Sandon Road and Lovatt Street. In function they corresponded in many respects to the textile mills, and this is reflected in the possession of three or four storeys and the regular spacing of the iron-framed windows. The works of the Stafford Box Co Ltd, Wogan Street, already there in 1881, have a special interest because a bridge at the centre crosses a side-street. Sleigh, a Stafford man, had been engaged to build one of the Stafford factories in 1858, and George Wormal, a Stafford architect, designed another in 1877. All the nineteenth-century Stafford shoe factories have now been converted to other uses.

CHAPTER THREE

Textiles

STAFFORDSHIRE is not generally associated with the textile industry, yet by the beginning of the nineteenth century a succession of mills stretched from the Cheshire to the Warwickshire border, taking advantage of the abundance of coal and of the power derived from the rivers Dove, Churnet, Trent and Tame. Good canal communications and a central position in between Manchester and Nottingham were added attractions. The raw materials were largely silk and cotton, but whereas the cotton industry was dispersed, the silk industry was orientated towards the Cheshire towns of Macclesfield and Congleton and was therefore concentrated in and near Leek, which of all the towns in Staffordshire is the one most dominated by the industrial monuments of the early nineteenth century.

There were silk workers at Leek in the seventeenth century, and at the end of the eighteenth century, when the products embraced sewing-silks, twist, buttons, ribbons, shawls and handkerchiefs, prosperity had reached a point where 2,000 were employed in the town itself and 1,000 in the surrounding countryside. By this time the towns of Macclesfield and Congleton had begun to adopt the factory system, but despite the turnpiking of the roads in 1762, and despite the opening of a branch canal in 1802, Leek continued to suffer from its comparative isolation.

It was not until the early nineteenth century that self-contained factories in which the functions of warehousing and manufacturing were combined began to appear at Leek. In the *Staffordshire Advertiser* of 29 July 1815 land at Barn Yates 'well adapted for the erection of Buildings for a large and extensive Manufactory', was offered for sale. Further particulars were obtainable from Mr Joseph Lowdnes who, significantly enough, was a Congleton man. Whether or not a factory was built at Barn Yates, the next fifteen years were ones of great development at Leek so that on 25 November 1826 the same paper could say that the town was 'flourishing and rapidly growing in size, the streets are spacious and in preparation to be lighted with gas'. The development may be related to two Acts of Parliament that markedly affected the English silk industry. First, in 1824, the high duty on imported raw silk was abandoned, and the duty on imported thrown silk was halved. Secondly, in 1826, foreign manufactured goods were admitted subject to a duty of only 35 per cent. The measures under the first Act provided an inducement to concentrate resources on the throwing rather than the weaving of silk, and because throwing was a part of the industry that lent itself to mechanisation, the construction of multi-storey mills gained momentum, only to be considerably retarded by the universal depression of the 1830s.

The architecture of the early nineteenth-century silk mills, so far as can be judged from surviving examples and pictorial records, was severely but effectively functional. They were about 100ft long, three to five storeys high and narrow enough for the span of a single oak beam. Trusses incorporated king-posts or queen-posts, bricks were the main walling material, stone being used only for plinths, sills, lintels and quoins; the cast-iron window frames had hinged opening lights, and the staircase was contained in a projection at the rear. Roofs were gabled or hipped, and were sometimes crowned at the centre with an elaborate cupola. This enclosed a bell for summoning work-people and was surmounted by a weather-vane and compass-points. It will be noted that there was no attempt at fireproof construction, and this continued to be so until the second half of the nineteenth century.

The power on which the multi-storey mills ultimately relied for the throwing, doubling, spinning, winding and weaving of silk was that of the steam engine. However, as late as 1825, only one mill in Leek had steam engines; the rest relied on human power. But by 1838 eight of the mills in Leek were powered by steam. Brampton Mill, Newcastle, was served by a 12hp engine; Cheddleton, and Badnall's, Leek, each had 6hp engines, and Eastwood Mill, Hanley, had a 4hp engine. The engine at Stone, also of 4hp, was by the ironfounders of that town, Rangeley & Diggles.

The stages that led to the adoption of the factory system are illustrated by the history of property on the east side of Pickwood Road in Leek. Black-a-Moors Head Lane, as Pickwood Road was called, runs between Derby Street and Brook Street (formerly Workhouse Lane), and parallel to St Edward Street (formerly Spout Street). In 1749 the buildings comprised the Buffalo's Head Inn on the Derby Street frontage, and the 'newly-erected twisting house' on the plot of ground at the back. Francis Beswick, button merchant, was the tenant. In 1764 Joseph Myott was twisting mohair in the twisting-house or shade, and in 1773 Phillips & Ford, button merchants, were stretching and drying mohair there. In 1797, when the ownership changed, silk was being worked as well as mohair.

John Fynney, the new partner, set to work to make more intensive use of the steep and cramped site, and between 1808 and 1826 he demolished the shade that had existed in 1749 and substituted a four-storey building which, when fully described in 1883, consisted of six dwellings and a warehouse on the three lower floors and a silk-twisting shade on the whole of the top floor. In addition John Fynney erected a 'spacious silk manufactory', the one that was assessed at £28 10s in 1834. Prosperity, however, came to a dramatic end. Ralph Moss and Isaac Brunt, silk manufacturers and carpenters, who had purchased most of the property for £2,300 in 1831, were declared bankrupt in 1834. The four-storey building erected by John Fynney still stands, but the 'spacious silk manufactory', three-storeys high, was demolished in 1967.

The term 'shade' has been applied to certain of the buildings in Pickwood Road. A 'shed' or 'shade' was a workshop where silk and other textiles were twisted. For this purpose the threads were hooked to the circumference of a large 'gate' or wheel and then passed round a 'cross' at the opposite end of the building. It was the work of boys known as Staffordshire trotters to run barefoot to and fro, carrying the

bobbins as they went. The distance between gate and cross might be
30yd, a roll was completed after 36 journeys, and 12 rolls might be
completed in a day. On the basis of these figures the boy ran nearly
15 miles a day.

The shade seems to have been the earliest form of building specially
identified with the silk industry. In 1781, according to the Land Tax
Return, three houses in Leek had shades attached, and by 1784 the
number had risen to five. They would all have been in the ancient
town centre; and the one owned by John Daintry, for instance, was
successively occupied by William Carr and Josiah Gaunt, two names
famous in the introduction of the factory system. The movement
from shade to multi-storey mill was symptomatic, but it should not be
supposed that the mill entirely superseded the shade. The two types of
building could be and were complementary. In 1834 Thomas Carr,
Ellis Russell & Co and Anthony Ward all occupied shades as well as
mills, and at the same time as many as twenty-three shades or groups
of shades were individually assessed for the levy of church rate. They
ranged in value from £30 to £4 10s. Far from being obsolete, shades
were still being built in the 1840s.

Architecturally, shades were divisible into two groups. There were
those like the one in Pickwood Road which comprised the top floor of a
row of dwellings; there were the others which were self-contained
buildings. The latter were of two storeys or more and could approxi-
mate with confusing closeness to the multi-storey mill. Because of
their industrial use and because of their relatively small scale and poor
construction, self-contained shades have been particularly prone to
destruction, but one that survived until 1963 stood as part of a housing
complex in Petty France, Leek. It was brick and tiled, 70ft long × 18ft
wide, and had two floors in addition to a semi-basement. An inscribed
brick gave the date of the original part of the building as 1832, and it
was presumably the 'twisting shade' that was first assessed for the levy
of church rate in 1835. The annual value was £11 14s. A building such
as this shade represents an intermediate stage between the factory
system on the one hand and the domestic system on the other. Steam

power was not used, but a long unencumbered floor area, suggesting factory conditions, was required.

The part of the industry that did remain purely domestic longest was the broad-weaving. This weaving was done on the top floors of private houses which were therefore three storeys high and, whereas the lower storeys were of conventional design, the different purpose of the top floor was evidenced externally by the windows, which were elongated to admit plenty of light and so to facilitate co-ordination of hand and eye. Ventilation was effected with sliding frames. Houses of this design may be seen in Stafford Street, Stone, and at Cheddleton, but by far the greatest number is in Leek which as late as 1962 retained over a hundred examples. They were always in attached groups of two or more, fronting the street, or at right angles to it and fronting a yard. The main concentrations are now in King Street, Albion Street and Broad Street, but there are also some in Fountain Street, London Street and Ashbourne Road.

Unlike the twisting-shade, a weaving place was small and compact, and enough space was provided by two houses together at uniform height. A typical arrangement was presented by four dwelling-houses in Mill Street, Leek. They were erected just before 1835 and had 'two spacious Weavers' Rooms over the same'. The appearance of such a building was indicated by the pair of houses that were demolished in 1968 having eventually become known as Nos 2 and 4, Court No 2, Wood Street, Leek. They had two elongated windows on either side of the top floor. Adjoining this pair of houses was a further pair, Nos 6 and 8, which were entirely devoted to living accommodation and were of two storeys only. In 1823 the land on which the two pairs stood was bought by William Thompson, broad-silk weaver, from Thomas Carr, silk manufacturer, and by January 1824, six dwellings had been erected. It will be noted that the number was six, not the final four: this is because Nos 2 and 4 were originally two pairs of back-to-back houses. The undertaking to convert them from four dwellings into two was not made until 1934, and even after that date the four substantial external doors betrayed their original duality.

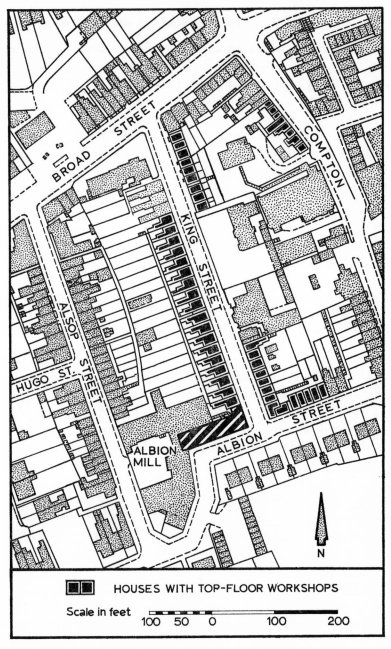

HOUSES WITH TOP-FLOOR WORKSHOPS

Scale in feet   100   50   0   100   200

King Street, Leek. Based on survey 1962 and Ordnance Survey map,
1 : 2500 (1966), Crown Copyright reserved

Each family in Nos 2 and 4 occupied two rooms both measuring about 13ft × 10ft; above extended the workshop which was not integrated with the living accommodation. Instead it was reached by its own staircase and its own external door. Nos 6 and 8, separated at ground-floor level by a tunnel passage, offered slightly better conditions, and it would have been in one of these houses that William Thompson lived. In 1851 altogether 31 persons occupied Nos 2–8, Court No 2. Of the 18 of working age, 10 were engaged in the silk industry, including a 6-year-old engine turner and William Thompson's wife, who was likewise a silk weaver. She was born in Macclesfield, indicating the continuity of the close relationship between Leek and other silk towns, but most of the other occupants were born either in Leek or had moved in from the adjoining agricultural areas, tempted by the higher wages offered by industry. Despite his ownership of the property, William Thompson was illiterate and marked his will with a cross. The organisation in such a weaving place would have corresponded to that originally current in a shade. That is to say the 'undertaker'—in this case William Thompson—would have obtained his raw material from the warehouseman. Journeymen and apprentices did the work and then the finished goods were returned to the warehouseman.

Finally the goods might have to be dyed. There were two dyers at Leek in 1784, and this was still the number in 1834 when the three dye-houses of William Hammersley were assessed at a total of £128 12s 6d. The dyeworks had to be near a plentiful supply of water, and although the eighteenth- and nineteenth-century buildings have largely disappeared, the location by the River Churnet has continued. Joshua Wardle Ltd at Leekbrook signify the range of their activity with the device of a raven and a rainbow; and Sir Thomas & Arthur Wardle Ltd at Bridge End commemorate in their first name the man who with his wife founded the Leek School of Embroidery in 1874. Their members put to good effect the art of indigo dyeing that he and William Morris worked together to recover.

During the nineteenth century, the importance of the factory as the manufacturing unit increased; Wellington Mills and London Mills,

Page 53　*Associations with Arkwright and Peel:* (above) *cotton mill at Rocester built by Richard Arkwright in the late eighteenth century;* (below) *Robert Peel's cotton mill at Fazeley, late eighteenth century*

Page 54 *Albion Mill, Leek. Established in 1815 as a silk mill, the same firm now manufactures industrial threads from manmade and natural fibres*

both dating from 1853, illustrate this trend. They are not noticeably different, except in scale, from their predecessors, but with their central pediment they are architecturally more self-conscious. Big Mill of about 1860 is especially impressive, but it is still predominantly of timber and masonry. It is the work of William Sugden who, with his son, was responsible for a number of industrial buildings in Leek. The only other example of their work that survives is the ponderously detailed warehouse of Brough, Nicholson & Hall, occupying the triangular site between Cross Street and Well Street. This warehouse is of fireproof construction. So, too, are Waterloo Mills, Waterloo Street, which date from 1894 and resemble Big Mill in their general design; but the pyramidal roof of the tower and the extensive window areas create a much lighter, whimsical effect.

In the twentieth century, the great change at Leek has been not so much in the architecture as in the finished product. Artificial fibres have almost entirely taken the place of silk, but the nineteenth-century buildings remain—a reminder of the days when Prussian bindings, braids, galloons, ferrets and bandannas were a source of livelihood.

COTTON

The history of the Staffordshire cotton industry differs in two notable respects from that of the silk industry. First, the factory system was introduced earlier and, secondly, it was developed more intensively. When in 1766 Thomas Bowers, cotton manufacturer of Eccleshall, proposed to establish a cotton manufactory for the employment of the Uttoxeter poor, hand spinning-wheels would have been in use. But this was just the time that James Hargreaves and Richard Arkwright were revolutionising the textile industry and it was significant for Staffordshire that when, in the late 1760s, both the inventor of ¡he 'spinning jenny' and the patentee of the 'water-frame' were driven by rioters out of Lancashire, the place to which they moved was Nottingham. For the remainder of the century the influence of both the East Midlands and Lancashire was felt in Staffordshire.

D

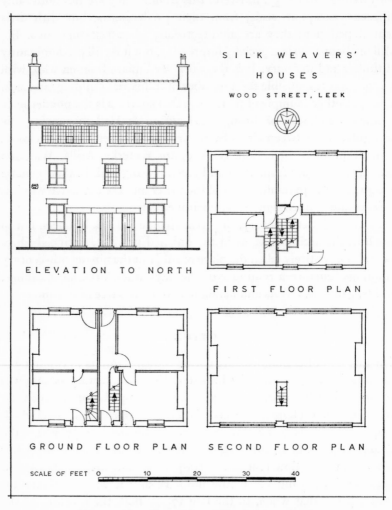

SILK WEAVERS' HOUSES

WOOD STREET, LEEK

ELEVATION TO NORTH

FIRST FLOOR PLAN

GROUND FLOOR PLAN

SECOND FLOOR PLAN

SCALE OF FEET 0 10 20 30 40

Nos 2 and 4, Court No 2, Wood Street, Leek

One of the two earliest cotton factories in the county, that at Rocester, was built in 1781–2 by Richard Arkwright himself, while John Cooper who co-owned the Mayfield Mill, was related by marriage to the Derbyshire cotton-spinning family of Strutt. But the stronger influence came direct from Lancashire. When, in 1779, his cotton-spinning machinery at Altham near Blackburn was destroyed by rioters, Robert Peel decided to move to Burton-on-Trent and there he built three cotton mills. The first, at Upper Mill immediately south of Burton, was opened in 1780 and comprised four main rooms, 74ft × 28ft; the other two, at Winshill and Bond End, dated from 1781 and 1784 respectively.

Presumably it was the success of the Burton enterprise that prompted Robert Peel's son, also called Robert and father of the future prime minister, to choose Tamworth and Fazeley as the centre of his cotton works. More than this, he made his home at nearby Drayton Manor. The first mill at Tamworth was opened in 1791 and it was followed in 1795 by a mill at Fazeley. At the same time the Staffordshire centres were themselves responsible for further proliferation within the county. In 1797 Peel's superintendent at Burton, Richard Thompson, built a mill at Newcastle and, shortly before 1793, two Burton brewers invested in a mill at Alrewas. But the limits of expansion were soon reached. Alrewas Mills were intended to be razed to the ground in 1819, and although they continued after this date they were occupied in 1834 by a wire-drawer, a corn miller and a lace-thread doubler. William and John Fowler, who were corn millers, paper makers, cotton spinners, dealers and chapmen at Alder Mills, Tamworth, were declared bankrupt in 1818. Castle Mills, Tamworth, were by 1821 used exclusively for corn grinding. Upper Mill, Burton, was a screw manufactory by 1844.

One consequence of the early adoption of the factory system for cotton manufacture was the reliance on water power. Whereas the silk factories were mainly in town centres, the cotton mills were by rivers and were therefore often in a rural setting. The mill at Rocester eventually had three waterwheels; that at Bond End, Burton, was served by a channel known as Peel's Cut; those at Mayfield and Tutbury were judiciously sited on the River Dove; and at Alrewas, Alton, Burton, Fazeley and Tamworth there was the further asset of a nearby canal. Nevertheless water supply was always unpredictable, and it was supplemented or superseded by steam. In 1791 Peel Yates & Co were buying from Boulton & Watt a 26hp sun and planet engine for their Burton mill at Bond End. As early as 1815 a 45hp engine was at work at Alrewas Mill. Thompson's mill at Newcastle was on the canal rather than a river so it needed a steam engine even from the beginning.

The Staffordshire cotton mills varied greatly in size. In 1815 the Alrewas Mill contained 80 carding machines, over 4,000 water or throstle spindles, about 800 spindles for doubling and twisting yarn and 50 power looms. The Rocester mill had 133 carding machines and 7,151 spindles. But the mill at Alton had only 1,152 spindles. The scale of capital investment involved in the construction of these large cotton mills and ancillary buildings is conveyed by the figures at Tamworth and Fazeley: for insurance purposes the mill at Tamworth was valued at £5,000; the printworks at Lady Meadow, Tamworth, and the mill at Bonehill were valued at £2,000 and £1,500 respectively. Of course, the sums were not entirely attributable to the buildings. When, following a fire at Fazeley, the property at Bonehill was covered by a new insurance policy in 1823, the total value was £21,700; £13,790 was for stock, £1,310 for machinery, and only £6,600 for buildings.

The relative cheapness of the buildings is partly to be explained by the austerity of the architecture. The mills erected by the Peels were especially plain, and it has been suggested that the lack of any refinement was a manifestation of asceticism. Arkwright's mill at Rocester did at least have rusticated quoins where it would be most seen by the public while Thompson's mill at Newcastle was embellished with both pediment and cupola. Many of the Staffordshire cotton mills were completed too early to take advantage of the improvements effected by William Strutt in Derbyshire: they are not of fireproof construction. But when the mill at Tutbury was enlarged about 1829, cast-iron columns supported cast-iron beams and brick vaults, and the same technique was also partly used at Mayfield.

Because of the retraction of the cotton industry in Staffordshire many of the earlier buildings have disappeared. Alrewas Mill which now grinds flour has been rebuilt, and the only surviving Burton mill is the one at Winshill. For the same reason the 'Steam Mill' at Fazeley is one of the few outstanding cotton buildings of the second half of the nineteenth century.

It has been mentioned that the early mills were often in rural settings. The need for self-contained communities was therefore even greater than usual. The mills at Alrewas, Mayfield, Rocester and Tutbury were lit from their own gasworks, and two of the mills at Burton had schools attached to them. Mayfield provides a classic example of a settlement built within the precincts of a mill, and good rows of three-storey workers' housing may be seen at Fazeley and Rocester. The living quarters at Alrewas in 1815 comprised 'a large commodious House for the reception of Apprentices, 12 Cottages or Tenements for work people, and a very pleasant and convenient Messuage fit for the residence of a Principal Superintendent of the concern' (*Staffordshire Advertiser*, 11 February 1815).

LINEN TAPE

Impressive though the remains of the cotton and silk industry are in Staffordshire, yet the greatest single monument belongs to another branch of the textile industry. The weaving of linen tapes at Upper Tean (Checkley), is associated with John and Nathaniel Philips, the sons of a local squire. In 1747, they persuaded van Sanfort, a Dutch-man, to come and show them how to construct 'swivel looms'. This, the traditional story, seems to have some basis, for a man named van Sanfort was in Manchester in 1750, and in 1755 it was possible for the brothers to write that money had been sunk 'in bringing over and pay-ing the Dutchman we had, and in altering and improving our looms'.

The subsequent history of tape-weaving at Tean was determined by the special conditions that characterised the textile industry. There was only limited need for centralisation. A manager's house was provided by Tean Hall, a half-timbered house that had been erected in 1613 and to which a brick and stone wing was added in the early eighteenth century. Buildings for storage, some production and maintenance were gradually added on the adjoining land, and in the early nineteenth century these comprised the 'old loom house', presumably dating from soon after 1737, and estimated to cost £160; the 'new loom house' of 1774; and the 'new warehouse' of 1775. Some of these buildings may be assumed to form part of the present finishing shop running west of Tean Hall along the High Street. This range is shown by straight joints in the brickwork to be of at least four different dates, the earliest part being that at the centre with remains of a stone footing. Eventually the front elevation was given some semblance of cohesion by the addition of a pediment containing a clock-dial. This pediment may have been built in 1816, the date inscribed on the clock movement. The cupola surmounted by compass-points and weather-vane, which so splendidly adorns the roof, seems to be even later since the bell contained in the cupola is inscribed with the date 1833.

Most of the production at Tean was dispersed: it was carried out on looms set up in cottages or in small loom-sheds attached to cottages. When in 1810 a register of all the looms was compiled, there were 429. Of these 217 were at Tean, 129 at Cheadle, 40 at Kingsley, 8 at Draycot and 35 at places unspecified. The number of looms per weaver ranged from 1 to 10.

By about 1820 the introduction of steam power was making itself felt, and J. & N. Philips & Co, as the firm was then called, began investigating how such power was being used by their competitors. They also got George Augustus Lee of Manchester to assess the financial advantages that might accrue to themselves. It was found that in December 1821 they possessed 465 looms of which 350, valued at £10 each, were at work. The cost of a single building to contain 450 looms was estimated at £6,400. To this amount had to be added £3,600 for the engine, boiler house, etc, £2,000 for the mill gearing etc, and £1,500 for the gas apparatus. This gave a total of £13,500. Depreciation and recurrent costs, comprising payment of loan interest, purchase of coal and attendance, were estimated at £2,250 per annum. A single building would facilitate maintenance of the looms but the greatest advantage would, of course, be the reduction in the labour force. It was noted that the wages of the 450 weavers, at 12s each per week, amounted to £270: if steam power were introduced, the number of weavers could be halved and the wages bill would fall to £135 per week. Recurrent costs would add £45, giving a total of £180. The saving that would result from steam power would therefore be the difference between £270 and £180 per week, ie £90 per week or £4,680 per annum.

The same simple arithmetic was used by Lee to estimate the cost of erecting a single building to contain all the looms. For this purpose he assumed that the building would be fireproof, 41ft 6in wide, and that it would be divided into bays, 8ft 6in long. Each bay of each floor would require four cast-iron beams weighing together 12cwt and costing £7 8s. They would be supported by three columns weighing together 8¼cwt and costing £5 18s. Bricks for the arches would cost £4 14s. Labour and other items excluding contingencies would bring the total to £32 10s.

Encouraged by these calculations it is no wonder that the company went ahead with conversion to steam power. However, instead of a single building, they decided on two, one to be at Tean and the other at Cheadle. Construction of the two mills seems to have gone on simultaneously so that in the records it is not always clear which one is being referred to.

The new mill at Tean ran back at right-angles from the main buildings that already existed, and until about 1950 it still contained some of the looms that, judged by their design, may well have been built soon after 1747. The only modification imposed by adaptation to steam power was the substitution of pulleys for the 'bar'. Despite the introduction of modern machinery, the new mill at Tean retains nearly all its original features and is by far the finest building of its kind in

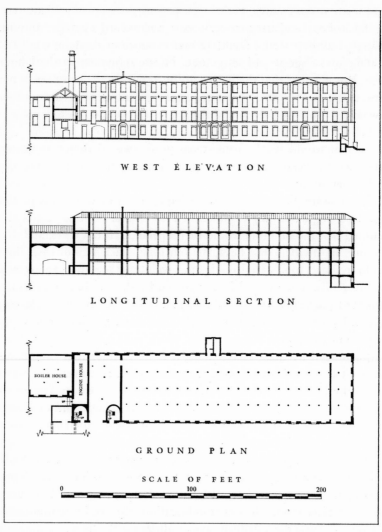

WEST ELEVATION

LONGITUDINAL SECTION

BOILER HOUSE
ENGINE HOUSE

GROUND PLAN

SCALE OF FEET

0   100   200

Steam-powered mill, Upper Tean, Checkley

Staffordshire. It is 217ft long × 51ft wide, and four storeys high. The basic design assumed by Lee was followed so that it illustrates the ultimate phase in cast-iron construction. The main part of the building is divided by 3 rows of 22 cast-iron columns into spaces for a total of 88 looms per floor or 352 altogether. The columns support cast-iron beams that in turn support brick vaults. On all but the top floor, the columns of two cross-rows have openings at the top intended to receive shafting, and where this is so, a pair of columns is substituted for a single one in the centre row.

The windows have the usual cast-iron frames, and the roof is so constructed as to present a uniform pitch when viewed from the ground. In fact there are valleys above each row of columns, and rainwater drains into some of the latter. At the north end of the mill two bays are separated by a cross-wall, and here is sited the main staircase that gives access to all the floors. Beyond, at the extreme north end is the engine house and a second staircase. The first steam engine was a 40hp one of double-acting beam construction and of 6ft stroke, replaced by a 90hp horizontal one in 1895. It was supplied by Boulton & Watt of Birmingham, whose earliest drawing of it is dated August 1822.

A special interest of the north end of the mill is that over this part only the original cast-iron roof trusses remain, and over the staircases they are exposed. They are a single casting, where the segmental arch is separated from the 'rafters' by a series of openwork circles of diminishing size. Slots in the 'rafters' receive the three pairs of purlins.

By December 1822, the mill had been 'raised to within a day's work of the square of the top story' when a violent storm inflicted damage estimated at £4,000. It was evidently completed about 1823, for this is the date inscribed on the centre pediment on the west side. There are three pediments to each side, and the wall for the corresponding length is stepped forward. The corners of the mill are strengthened by buttresses channelled vertically, but otherwise the effect of the mill is derived from its size and from the regular spacing of the windows. The name of the contractor is not known for certain, but it was probably James Trubshaw, builder and engineer of Haywood near Stafford. He witnessed a contract in 1822, and ale was given to the workmen by 'Mr. Trubshaw's' order in December 1821.

Since 1823 the expansion and redevelopment of Tean Hall Mills has continued, and the evidence of steam power is now largely confined to the remains of shafting on the top floor of the rear of the early High Street range. Among additions is the No 1 Shed of 1876, and the building that incorporates the inner of the two archways leading from the High Street. A brick dates it to 1829 and it was in use as a stove in about 1836. An even more notable addition is the four-storey 'New Finishing Rooms', complete with pyramidal-roofed air-duct, heavy cornice continuing round the pilasters and central pediment. Dated 1884–5 and forming the west end of the High Street frontage, these buildings may have been designed by William Sugden & Son of Leek who are known to have built artisans' dwellings for the company at Cheadle.

The concentration of looms under one roof affected the children. Now that their mothers were no longer at home there was no one to care for them, so the section of the mill that had previously been a weaving shop and warehouse was occupied partly as a school, and even unweaned children were catered for. They were brought through a doorway, now blocked, at the Tean Hall end of the street frontage, and so to a hatch. This hatch, pierced with a hole large enough to accommodate a breast, may still be seen.

The other settlement dominated by the firm of J. & N. Philips was Cheadle where they had the second of their steam-powered mills. This made use of the same patterns for the iron castings, it likewise abutted earlier buildings and had a Boulton & Watt engine. The mill itself, 114ft long × 51ft wide, three storeys high and with three rows of columns providing spaces for a total of 140 looms, was largely demolished in 1973. The warehouse extension fronting Tape Street and constructed in the same way survives. The elevations at Cheadle lacked the refinements to be found at Tean although the warehouse has a central pediment.

Besides being weavers, J. & N. Philips were also bleachers and dyers. From about 1750 that part of their business was carried on by itself, at The Croft, Upper Tean, where there was spring water for processing and running water for power. Adaptation to a welding works in 1971 resulted in considerable changes, but only to the interior of the most notable building. This was the stove, 66ft long × 31ft wide, where the drying took place on carriages that ran along rails from the loading section at the one end to the heating section at the other. Inscribed bricks above the entrance give the date of the stove as 1841 and name the owners (John & Nathaniel Philips & Co), the manager of Tean Hall Mills (Joseph Wood), the bleacher (William Travis), the architect (James Whitaker), the builders (William & Samuel Waugh), and the brickmaker (Richard Stanier). They also record that the bricks were made on Tean church land. Other surviving features at The Croft include one bay of the pre-1836 'kier-shed' where the tapes were boiled and washed, the ground floor of the 1829 bleach-house, a stack of 1841 and a warehouse of 1889. To the west, on open ground extending to the River Tean, linen tapes were spread to be bleached by the sun until the 1930s.

Finally the influence of the Philips firm was felt in their attitude towards living conditions and social amenities. The impact of the introduction of steam power was vividly illustrated by 'Double Row' in Tean—a terrace of eight cottages built in 1798. Each would have had a set of four looms on the ground floor, and the living accommodation on the upper floor was approached by external stone staircases at the rear. With removal of the looms to the mill, the ground floor could be converted to living accommodation for a further eight tenants and their families. 'Double Row' was demolished in 1966, and the best workers' cottages are now Nos 1–8, Holborn Row, boldly numbered on the door lintels. Two octagonal privies, divided into eight units and with a central ventilator resembling a chimney-stack, stand behind Nos 1 and 3, New Road, and Nos 4–12, Old Road. A church of 1843, a Providence chapel of 1822, a Wesleyan chapel of 1843 and a school of 1855–6, show how the Philips family provided for spiritual and educational welfare. And a mile away stands their mansion, Heath House, rebuilt in 1836–40 by Thomas Johnson, the Lichfield architect. The complex is thus completed in the same way as Drayton Manor once completed the complex at Tamworth, Fazeley and Bonehill.

CHAPTER FOUR

Malting and Brewing

SUCH has been the effect of the tied-house system and of competition from the large-scale operator that the inn offering home-brewed beer is now a rare survival. But at one time innkeepers were not only brewers but occasionally maltsters as well. In 1836 the New Inn at Gnosall had both a malthouse and a brewhouse adjoining the house, and when the Lamb & Flag at Little Haywood near Stafford was offered for sale in 1838 the premises included a brewery and a three-storey malthouse. The floor of the malthouse, when not spread with barley, provided an additional dining-room for a club that patronised the inn. Of the 8 innkeepers at Eccleshall in 1834, 2 were also maltsters; and at Walsall the corresponding figures were 68 and 7. Malting as traditionally practised requires a large floor area. The land for this purpose was not always available, in which case the innkeeper acquired his malt from elsewhere and established a satisfactory vertical integration by confining his activities to brewing and the serving of the finished product. Specialist malsters were therefore more plentiful than their brewing counterparts, and all Staffordshire towns and most large villages had at least one malster in 1834.

MALTHOUSES

Typical of more prosperous maltsters was the one at Bond End, Yoxall. His business accounts have survived, and the earliest readily legible ones, those for 1806, show that during that year 2,301 bushels of malt were sold, the usual rate being 11s a bushel. The largest amount, 298$\frac{1}{2}$ bushels, was sold in February, and the smallest, 86 bushels, in June. The variation corresponds to the interruption in the malting and brewing cycle caused by the temperature being too high in the summer for controlled germination of the barley, and too hot for fermentation of the ale. The customers were notably the nobility and clergy who, being household brewers, escaped the beer tax. The innkeepers, whether local or as far afield as Birmingham, were relatively unimportant. The sale of malt was the chief source of income, and the chief expenditure was, of course, on barley, which in 1806 cost between about 5s and 6s a bushel. During the year about 2,000 bushels of barley coming from farms within a radius of 10 miles was bought. Other purchases included nearly 4cwt of hops bought from 'Mr. Webster' of Lichfield—the Yoxall maltster was also a hop merchant—and six loads of coke to fire the kiln.

The brick and tiled malthouse at Bond End survives, although it is now used as a builder's store, and the kiln was partly demolished in 1968. The main part running parallel with the road is three-storeys high, 83ft long and 21ft wide. The upper two floors are laid with gypsum plaster, a material mentioned by Plot as being used for this purpose in the late seventeenth century and which, because of its ability to be kept clean and sweet, commended itself as late as the 1870s. There are two loading doors at first-floor level. The kiln forming a cross-wing at the west end is shown by an inscription on one of the tie-beams to have dated from 1776.

The functions of the Bond End malthouse are best interpreted by considering two similar malthouses that were described when that indefatigable student of breweries, Alfred Barnard, visited Crown Street, Stone, in 1888. The western malthouse at Stone survives as a store. It is altogether 102ft long × 23ft wide and is divided structurally to correspond with the four main stages in the malting process: storage and germination of the barley, and curing and storage of the malt. The main part at the south end is three-storeys high, and the ground floor is the 'growing' or 'withering floor' which in Barnard's day was laid with blue brick and, in accordance with the usual practice, was sunk below the ground as much as 10ft, thereby securing a humid atmosphere for the germination of the barley. The two floors above, are each divided into two almost equal compartments by what was originally an end wall. External doors at first- and second-floor levels, and manually operated hoists above these doors, enabled receipt of the barley and discharge of the malt.

Finally at the north end of the malthouse, unrelated to the three-floor division of the remainder, is the kiln, where the malt was cured. It measures 21ft square internally. The only external evidence of its former function is the absence of windows, the door for admission of the fuel and the tie-rod plates inscribed 'CROSSKEY, LICHFIELD' that proclaim the exceptional stresses to which the brickwork has been subjected. Inside, however, the peculiarities of the architecture are immediately evident. The furnace has been removed from the square central chamber, but the floor above is still laid with the characteristic tiles perforated in such a way as to allow the heat to pass upwards but to prevent the grains of malt falling through. The furnace chamber is surrounded on all four sides by a 3ft wide passage, used for storage of the fuel. This is half-arched in brick but low enough to ensure that the heat from the fire could rise above the upper surface of the vault and reach the full extent of the floor above.

The second malthouse in Crown Street, Stone, measured 103ft × 19ft, the width being determined as elsewhere by the size of beams that carried the floors and roof. The 12qr steep, 6ft square, remained at the south-west corner, and the furnace comprised a simple iron basket set on three walls of brickwork. The building was largely intact until demolished in 1964.

The earliest malthouses, like those at Yoxall and Stone, resembled barns for they were disproportionately long with the kiln at one end. A more compact plan was achieved if the malthouse could be doubled in width, but the objection then was the amount of space that was taken by the intermediate supports. A malthouse in Station Street, Burton, was encumbered with a series of wide brick piers and, as Barnard commented, it belonged to a time when land was cheap and when loss of space was the least consideration of the maltsters. Stafford malthouse, dated 1837, survives, and here it is only the first floor that is supported by brick piers; the ground floor or basement is like the crypt of a church with a series of arches resting on stone columns. This malt-house at Stafford can be compared with that at Upper St John Street, Lichfield, which is dated 1858. The basic plan of the two malthouses is similar; the great difference lies only in the choice of materials. At Lichfield the upper floor is supported by wooden beams and five rows of cast-iron columns, and in this way a structure more resistant to fire and with a higher proportion of workable floor area has been produced.

In Burton malthouses conformed to a standard design, illustrated by four dated 1864 in Wetmore Road. The barley was hoisted on to the top floor, and after being screened it was dropped into the barley garners and then into a long tank with brick sides and a sloping false bottom of perforated tiles. After steeping, the barley was thrown into the couching-frame where it remained twenty-four hours. The next process, the flooring, took place on three floors one above the other, hoists being used to raise the barley-loaded skips. All the barley, now called 'green malt', was collected on the top floor before passing into the kiln, and in the final part of the malthouse the cured malt was screened and stored. The barley thus moved progressively through the build-ing, and the two hoists for loading and unloading were at opposite ends.

The iron columns decreased in size from floor to floor as the weight they carried decreased, and those in the working floors, forming a grid as they did, had the incidental function of helping the maltster measure the movement of his barley. Timber was retained for the intermediate beams and for the three rows of queen-post roof trusses that spanned all but the kiln. The frames of the windows were of wood and, as it was important to have maximum control over the admission of air, the windows in the working floors were specially designed and were often of two lights pivoted about their centres horizontally. Kiln roofs varied greatly and were a feature that especially contributed to the architectural distinctiveness. Sometimes as at Wetmore Road, there were two transverse gabled ridges, but equally there might be a single hipped roof or two or four pyramidal roofs. Ventilation was pro-vided by louvres running along the ridge or by cowls or by a combina-tion of the two. A second opportunity for variety lay in the design of the

Page 71　*Steam Mill, Fazeley. Erected in 1883 beside the Birmingham &
Fazeley Canal, this cotton mill represents the ultimate in textile mill
construction*

Page 72 *Domestic brewhouse of the Earls of Lichfield at Shugborough.*
Now part of the County Museum

projecting hoist platforms which could be elaborately decorated in cast iron. Otherwise the architecture relied for effect on the panelling and on the relationship of brick and stone to openings. Datable maltings at Burton which adequately illustrate late nineteenth-century design are those of Bass at Shobnall (1873–91), of Worthington in Hay Walk (1876), of Cross Street Brewery in Park Street (1877), of the Executors of Peter Walker in Clarence Street (1883), and of Richards, Cherry & Yeomans in Shobnall Street (1897–8).

Some of these maltings were attached to breweries but others, like those at Wetmore Road and Shobnall, occupied sites away from the breweries and did so only because the land here was cheaper and because the new railway system reduced the disadvantage of isolation. Given a large virgin site, it was possible to have a range of six or eight malthouses, and these might be grouped so closely together that a bridge at barley-store level spanned the gaps. The size of these late nineteenth-century malthouses may be judged from the capacity of the steeps. It was quite usual for 180 or 150qr of barley to be steeped at one time, in marked contrast to the 8qr steeps of the early nineteenth century.

The use of cast iron made practicable the very large building, but what put a premium on size was the availability of steam power. All later maltings were served by a steam engine, and at Walsitch, for instance, the engine house occupies a prominent central position. The power was needed to pump the steeping water from wells into the tank and to drive the hoists and the machinery that screened the barley. Yet there were still other ways in which some maltsters tried to apply the use of steam. For instance, at Bindley's maltings the kiln floor was unloaded by Archimedean screw, and at Worthington's malthouse of 1876 the loading was effected by an 'aerial railway' radiating from the entrance to the kiln. At Clarence Street Brewery the turning of the malt was mechanised, which involved the construction of kilns that were circular internally. The final development came when steam power was used for turning the barley, and for this to be possible the barley was no longer worked on the floor but rotated in box drums.

E

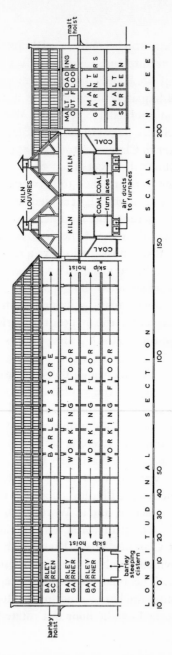

Malthouse, Burton-upon-Trent. Based on architect's drawing for Bass, Ratcliff & Gretton Ltd, undated, in possession of Bass Charrington

One of the earliest buildings designed to accommodate box drums was Bass's Plough Maltings of 1902–4, and once there had been this development the need for large floor areas was considerably reduced. Nevertheless floor malting continued at Burton until the 1960s and was still being practised at Wombourne in 1970. With the abandonment of the flooring technique and with the concentration of the malting industry, brewers, such as Joule's of Stone and Butler's of Wolverhampton, gave up the malting part of their business. Some malthouses have been converted to new uses, often disassociated from brewing, and others have been demolished. In Uttoxeter the malthouse that dominated the centre of the town was demolished in 1968, and in 1970 the Trent Valley Maltings at Lichfield suffered the same fate. At Burton the rate of change during the 1960s was particularly noticeable.

BREWERIES

The main consumer of malt was the brewer and, as the records of the Yoxall maltster suggest, a not inconsiderable part of the early brewing was carried on at the houses of the landed families. Every great house had its own brewhouse, and a good Staffordshire example is provided at Shugborough where the brewhouse of the Earls of Lichfield forms part of the County Museum. Externally the windows are shuttered rather than glazed. Internally there are two vats, 7ft and 5ft 9in diameter respectively, and although the lighter equipment has largely disappeared enough survives to illustrate one feature common to every brewery. This is the emphasis on height to take maximum advantage of gravitational flow. There are the remains of a hoist to raise materials, timber staging to provide differences in level and, most indicative of all, the remains of the sloping trays where the wort gradually cooled after being boiled and before descending into the fermenting vat (see also page 79).

Because of the role fulfilled by the great house on the one hand and by the inn on the other, the common brewery, producing beer for a wholesale market, was a comparative latecomer, and the early Staffordshire breweries, including even those at Burton, tended to be small concerns satisfying local custom. One such brewery was that at Shelton, established by William Malkin about 1823. In 1835 its equipment was valued at £1,021, and the more costly items included the copper (£86), two 'working vats' (£20), four portervats (£133 6s 8d), the malt-mill (£25), and two mash-tubs (£17). In addition there was an exciseman's desk and stool (16s), a hydraulic pump (£4 10s), a saccharometer (£3 10s) and a windlass and rope (£1 13s). The absence of steam power is noticeable, and it is a sign of the inferiority of the Staffordshire brewers that unlike those of London, Dublin and other centres of population they did not buy engines from Boulton & Watt. Instead, they continued to rely on water- or horse-power. Horninglow Brewery, Burton, and Barton Turn Brewery, Barton-under-Needwood, for instance, both seem to have done so in 1805 and 1812. More details are available about the brewery at Alton which had 'a good supply of excellent water at a required height (with large reservoirs), equal to the power required for grinding the malt during three parts of the year'. The grinding or crushing of the malt was one operation inviting mechanisation, and another was the pumping of the water into the brewing-copper. At Wolverhampton, in 1824, both operations were performed 'with ease by one horse'; but careful siting of the brewery could reduce the need for pumping, and it was a virtue of the Alton Brewery that because it was built against a hillside 'the great descent in the different processes' entirely took away 'all lifting and pumping to the carriage that may convey the liquor away'. The Alton Brewery was 'new-erected' in 1812, and it was apparently not until after this that steam engines began to be common in Staffordshire breweries. At Cheddleton a steam engine had been installed by 1844, while at Newcastle the engine was described as 'new' in 1824.

Although the Burton brewers may not have been pioneers in the use of steam power, nevertheless their rise to a national—or rather an international—level of importance coincides with the improvement of communications that was an essential part of the Industrial Revolution. Burton beer was well-known in London in the seventeenth century, but it was not until the middle of the next century that brewers like Benjamin Wilson, William Worthington, Henry Evans and William Musgrave were successful in exploiting the two special assets of Burton. These were, first and foremost, the high gypsum content of the well-water, and secondly the easy access to the port of Hull. Until 1770 the route was along the navigable River Trent, but after this date, with the opening of the east end of the Trent & Mersey Canal, the journey was divided in two; canal boats went as far as Gainsborough and schooners, as before, completed the journey to Hull. Once the beer was at Hull the relative cheapness of sea transport placed a world market virtually within the Burton brewers' reach. At first the chief importing countries were Russia, Sweden and Prussia, but closing of the Baltic ports in 1806 temporarily halted trade in this direction, and imposition of prohibitive tariffs finally did so between 1822 and 1826. The brewers were therefore compelled to turn elsewhere, and the most lucrative market proved to be India. The London India Ale was imitated with a success that, thanks to the Burton water, transcended even that of the original product, and the export figures of Bass and Allsopp were still rising when the most important single event in the industrial history of Burton took place. The opening of the Midland Railway in 1839 immediately eliminated the difference in cost between water transport and that by land. The way was clear for development of the home market, and such was the acknowledged supremacy of Burton water and the popularity of pale ale that the great London brewers started to establish outposts in Burton. Ind Coope, virtually a London firm, did so in 1856, and they were followed by Charrington, Truman, and Mann, Crossman & Paulin in 1871, 1873 and 1875 respectively.

Burton's rise to prosperity was so spectacular that, not surprisingly, surviving buildings do little to indicate the long association of the town with the brewing industry. Molyneux in 1869 commented that 'the old breweries of forty, or even twenty years ago, were comparatively speaking insignificant and inconvenient buildings, situated to the rear of private houses, or inns, and approached by a narrow passage from the High Street, down which all the ale and grains had to be rolled or carried by men and women, to the carts or waggons there placed ready to receive them'.

Instead of the insignificant and inconvenient buildings there arose ones that were solid, bold and capacious 'neither deficient nor conspicuous in architectural detail, but well and studiously arranged, covering an enormous area of ground'. Since Molyneux's day some of the brewers' houses, such as Nunneley's in Bridge Street and those of Bass and Evans in High Street, have been retained, but otherwise no significant part of the present breweries is any earlier than 1850. Some evidence of continuity was, however, provided by the siting of breweries in High Street, related as these were to the succession of private houses and to the grounds of these houses that ran back to the Hay Ditch.

The modern breweries that Molyneux particularly had in mind were Allsopp's New Brewery of 1859, Bass's Middle Brewery of 1853 and the same firm's New Brewery of 1864. The building activity increased in momentum after the publication of Molyneux's work, and other datable Burton breweries of the second half of the nineteenth century were: Ind Coope Brewery (1858–9), Abbey Brewery (1871–2), Black Eagle Brewery (1873), Bindley & Co (1873), Albion Brewery (1875), A. B. Walker & Sons (1877), Clarence Street Brewery (1883) and Cross Street Brewery (1883–8). The firm of Bass employed their own engineer to design their buildings, but others turned to private architects who specialised in commercial work. The most active in Staffordshire was George Scamell of Great George Street, Westminster, who besides being responsible for Black Eagle Brewery and Clarence Street Brewery also designed the City, Trent Valley and St John Street Breweries at Lichfield. The architects who enlarged the Worthington Brewery in 1880 were Evans & Jolly of Nottingham, and in the same town Martin & Hardy and W. & S. T. Martin were the architects of Abbey Brewery and Albion Brewery respectively. *The Builder* of 17 July 1858 shows that Allsopp's New Brewery was the work of Hunt & Stephenson of Westminster, Hunt being the same as the architect of Stoke-on-Trent railway station.

Despite any individual foibles or restrictions imposed by the site, the basic plan of the Burton breweries that were either newly erected or rebuilt in the second half of the nineteenth century is often the same. This plan was determined by the processes described by Molyneux in 1869 and illustrated by Bass's New Brewery of 1864. The malt, having been received from the malthouse and screened and crushed on the top floors of the brewhouse, fell into the mash-tun. Mixture with hot water released the saccharine properties of the malt and thus created the substance known as wort which first percolated into the under-back on the bottom floor and was then raised by pumps to the upper-back on the top floor. It passed through pipes to the coppers where it was boiled and where the hops were added, and after the hops had been drained off in hop-backs it remained for the wort to be cooled and for fermentation to take place. The cooling was performed in a series of shallow trays and then more rapidly in a refrigerator consisting of a long twisted pipe submerged in running water. The fermentation, procured with yeast, took place first in large wooden vessels, either round or square, and then in special cleansing casks peculiarly associated with Burton and known as union vessels. Swan-neck pipes took the yeast from these vessels into the barm trough, and finally the ale, as it had become, was run off into racking squares on the ground floor of the brewery. Meanwhile, various by-products had been obtained in the process of manufacture, and these—the spent malt grains, the spent hops and the discharged yeast—likewise found their way to the ground floor.

The functions of the late nineteenth-century brewery imposed a clear separation between the tall and multi-roofed brewhouse and the low more spacious fermenting house. At Burton, union-rooms could be of enormous size. That of Allsopp's impressed Barnard when he visited their New Brewery about 1887. It was 375ft long × 105ft wide × 21ft high and contained 1,624 union vessels. As with the malt-houses, such buildings demanded the use of cast iron, and indeed the

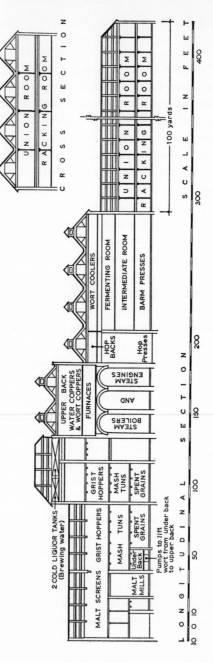

Brewery, Burton-upon-Trent. Based on drawing of New Brewery, undated, in possession of Bass Charrington

risk of fire often encouraged a completely cast-iron construction. The fermenting room of Allsopp's New Brewery had a roof of special elaboration, where there were four brick arches to each bay and where pierced cast-iron trusses, shaped to receive these arches, rose from cast-iron columns. But unless the fire risk was a decisive consideration the material used continued to be timber. Burton brewers had been timber-oriented ever since the days when Baltic oak for staves and building timbers had been bartered for ale in the eighteenth century.

The architecture of the Burton breweries may not have been distinctive, but their siting was the result of an extraordinary dependence on a railway system. A self-sufficient brewery consisted of far more than a brewhouse, fermenting house and maltings, and indeed a high proportion of the area was devoted to the storage of bulk commodities and to the stabling of horses. As early as 1869 the Burton breweries covered 174 acres, and there were as many as 76 ale-stores and 20 cooperages, quite apart from pumping-houses, water towers and offices. Transport of coal, coke, staves, casks, ale, malt, hops and barley accounted for much of a brewery's activity, and once the Midland Railway had arrived at Burton the ale was taken in horse-drawn two-wheel floaters to the station. But if the ale could be loaded direct on to railway trucks with twice the capacity of the floaters this would be far more convenient, and the reduced congestion on the roads would more than compensate for the delay occasioned by level-crossings. The Midland Railway Company obtained its first Act of Parliament to build lines across the roads in 1859, and so began a railway system that was eventually to extend about 50 miles. Every brewery had its railway link.

Because of the nineteenth-century development at Burton, earlier brewery buildings must be sought elsewhere. Many of the smaller breweries have long been defunct, but one feature that tends to remain is the brewer's house. As a plan of Longton Brewery or a view of North Staffordshire Brewery, Newcastle, shows, a typical layout allowed for a brewer's house on the road frontage. The house at Joule's Brewery at Stone (page 194) and the house at Crossley Stone Brewery, Rugeley,

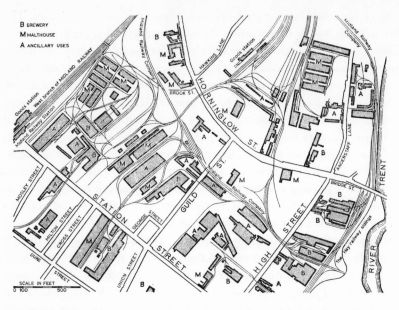

Relationship of brewery buildings to railway system, Burton-upon-Trent. Based on printed plan of Burton by Charles Harrison, 1870

both add architectural distinction to their respective towns. The former is now converted into an office, the latter was described in 1841 as 'an excellent modern built House' and may have been connected with a brewery that in 1826 was about to be established somewhere in the town. The house at Stone complements a brewery that probably has a longer continuous history than any other in Staffordshire. Appropriately enough the buildings reflect in their range of dates and in their layout the gradual growth and development of the company. Joule's, however, is the exception and generally, even away from Burton, the breweries tended to be late nineteenth-century establishments deliberately sited away from town centres. This is so of Springfield Brewery at Wolverhampton (page 204) and of the three principal ones at Lichfield. Bent's eight-storey brewery on the outskirts of Stone dates from 1888 and carries the tower design to its ultimate conclusion. Great as the changes were in the second half of the nineteenth century they have been eclipsed by those of a century later. The considerable increase in production has been accompanied by a decrease in the number of operating companies. Whereas there were 26 active in Burton in 1869, now, due partly to mergers, there are only 4. Concentration of ownership has led successively to the conversion of breweries to other uses and to their final destruction, and among the most recent to disappear are St John Street Brewery, Lichfield and, in Burton, Bass's (High Street), Bindley's (Station Street), Evershed's (Bank Square), Robinson's (Union Street) and Worthington's (Station Street).

Finally one of the characteristic sights of Burton has gone. In 1967 the internal railway system succumbed to the advent of the lorry, and now it is necessary to go to the County Museum at Shugborough to see one of the steam locomotives and the directors' carriage that were the pride of Bass's railway. The museum also contains examples of maltsters' and coopers' tools. The fact that brewery features of the early twentieth century have become museum exhibits is a striking indication of the changes that have taken place. Mechanisation has transformed most forms of industry, but for brewing it has done something more. With the departure of the ale-consuming navvy and all that he stands for, the market has changed, and in the second half of the twentieth century social conditions are epitomised by bright carbonated beers.

CHAPTER FIVE

Coal, Iron and Other Mineral Resources

COAL

COAL, iron and fireclay, all won from the same pit, are the minerals upon which the prosperity of Staffordshire so long depended. These were the resources that attracted to the county the potters and glassmakers and provided the inducement to improve roads and to build canals and railways. Not only were the minerals extensive, but for variety and accessibility they compared favourably with those of any other part of Britain.

The supremacy easiest to recognise is that of the Staffordshire coal. It is fair to generalise because the county is underlain by what is often thought of as one continuous coalfield, but in fact three areas of coal production—south Staffordshire, north Staffordshire and Cannock Chase—are conveniently separated. The south Staffordshire coalfield extends from Stourbridge in the south-west to Walsall in the north-east, and from Wednesfield in the north-west to West Bromwich in the south-east. By no accident the area came to be known in the nineteenth century as the Black Country. It is subdivided between Gornal and Rowley Regis by the Russell Hall Fault, to the south of which the measures are much more sharply folded and faulted. Throughout the field the great characteristic was the presence of twelve or fourteen seams lying so close together as to give the impression of a single bed of coal. It was appropriately called the Thick Coal or the Ten Yard Seam, and north of the Russell Hall Fault it was rarely more than 400ft below the surface. It presented a phenomenon unique in Great Britain.

The accessibility of the south Staffordshire coal was matched in the north by the number and variety of the workable seams. There are two main north Staffordshire coalfields. By far the larger occupies

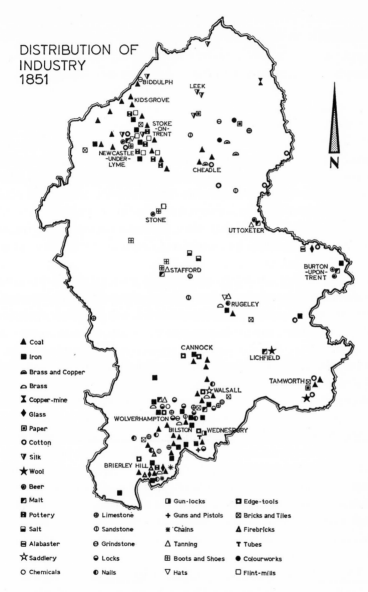

DISTRIBUTION OF INDUSTRY 1851

BIDDULPH
LEEK
KIDSGROVE
STOKE-ON-TRENT
NEWCASTLE-UNDER-LYME
CHEADLE
STONE
UTTOXETER
STAFFORD
BURTON-UPON-TRENT
RUGELEY
CANNOCK
LICHFIELD
WALSALL
TAMWORTH
WOLVERHAMPTON
BILSTON
WEDNESBURY
BRIERLEY HILL

N

▲ Coal
■ Iron
◓ Brass and Copper
◒ Brass
✗ Copper-mine
◆ Glass
▣ Paper
○ Cotton
▽ Silk
★ Wool
◉ Beer
▨ Malt
▣ Pottery
▤ Salt
▤ Alabaster
☆ Saddlery
○ Chemicals

⊕ Limestone
◑ Sandstone
⊖ Grindstone
◖ Locks
◐ Nails

▣ Gun-locks
✚ Guns and Pistols
✳ Chains
△ Tanning
⊞ Boots and Shoes
▽ Hats

▣ Edge-tools
⊠ Bricks and Tiles
▲ Firebricks
T Tubes
● Colourworks
▢ Flint-mills

Distribution of industries in Staffordshire. Based on White's
Staffordshire Directory, 1851

a triangular area centred on the Potteries, and it stretches from Biddulph in the north to Silverdale in the south-west and Longton in the
south-east. The main outcrop of long-flame coals, suitable for kiln-
firing, followed a line that is significantly enough revealed by the
position of the towns of Tunstall, Burslem, Hanley, Fenton and
Longton. The second field was much smaller and centred upon
Cheadle. Rich as the seams in both fields were, they were often
steeply pitched and subject to faulting so that conditions were as
variable in north Staffordshire as they tended to be constant in the
south. Between the two main coalfields of north and south Staffordshire lies a third that is separated from the south Staffordshire field
by the Bentley Faults. This is the Cannock Chase coalfield. Immediately south of the Faults the various seams of the Thick Coal had
become detached, and north of them the depth of the coal was increased by up to 360ft. Consequently in Cannock Chase the coal was
far less easily proved and won than in either the north or south.
Apart from the establishment of collieries near Brereton, Bloxwich
and Cheslyn Hay, the exploitation of the coalfield had to wait until
the 1850s.

The different characteristics of the various coalfields profoundly
influenced their individual histories. The exploitation of the south
Staffordshire coalfield is a sorry tale of wasteful short-sightedness.
Coal was being worked at Kingswinford by 1291, and at first attention would have been directed to the outcrops and the shallow seams.
Where there were shafts these were sunk until the Thick Coal was
reached, whereupon the seam was followed until it became unsafe to
undercut any further. The result of this method was to produce the
well-known bell-pit, so called because of the shape finally assumed.
Occasionally remains of these bell-pits are discovered. For instance,
when opencast mining was in progress at Dibdale, Lower Gornal,
the coal was found to have been disturbed by a regular pattern of
filled-in shafts. The shafts, 8ft apart, were 30ft deep, and although
they were 4ft 6in diameter at the surface they widened out at the
Thick Coal to a maximum of 9ft.

As early as 1710, however, depths of as much as 180ft were being reached, and already the problem that was increasingly to dominate the history of the south Staffordshire coalfield was being encountered —the riddance of flood water. The use of Savery's atmospheric engine near Wednesbury proved a failure, but in 1712 a Newcomen engine was installed at Conygree coalworks, Tipton, and exhibited for the first time the successful application of steam to the pumping of water. Later in the century, in 1776, there was a further innovation when Bentley Banner & Co bought from Boulton & Watt a pumping steam engine of unprecedented size. It was set up at the Bloomfield Colliery and in less than an hour emptied a pit 90ft deep containing 57ft of water. It had a 50in cylinder and a 7ft stroke.

The typical arrangement of a south Staffordshire pit in the nineteenth century was that described by Warington Smyth and others. There were two shafts, 6 to 8ft diameter, and 6 to 8yd apart. The shafts were generally lined with brickwork, and above each was a broad cast-iron pulley mounted in a head-frame. Ropes or, later, rattle chains of the kind still to be seen in Booth Street, Hednesford, passed over the two pulleys and were attached to a drum that was driven by a whimsey engine, and as a skip of coal was raised from one shaft an empty skip was lowered down the other. The same skips were also used to carry the men. At the bottom of the shaft a main road, 7 or 8ft wide, was cut through the lower part of the Thick Coal and gave access to the square workings which were formed by cutting two series of passages or stalls at right angles to one another. The lower seams were got first, and then followed the particularly dangerous operation of bringing down the upper seams with use of scaffolding and by means of picks and long iron prongs. Once the work had been completed all that was left was a grid of pillars, 8 or 10yd square, and a wall or rib of coal, 8 or 10yd thick, that separated one square from its neighbour. Below ground, horses drawing the skips along a railway were the source of power, but on the surface the steam engine predominated. The gin—where a rotating horse harnessed to a pole turned the axle of the drum—persisted, however, at the smaller pits and, when the General Strike of 1926 encouraged illicit mining, the use of gins was revived at Straits, Lower Gornal. Working of the coal by such wasteful and primitive methods created a landscape described by Smyth in 1853 as being dotted over 'with innumerable shafts, and deformed by the large waste heaps of slate and slack which so frequently surround them'. Flooding was the chief cause of trouble and in 1873, within the Tipton district alone, 120 engines were having to raise 36 million gallons of water a day. Things might have been different had not the ease of winning coal militated against the emergence of powerful companies. As it was, it was only towards the end that the search for deep deposits beyond the exposed coalfield necessitated an altogether different scale of operation. From 1874 there were winnings at such places as Sandwell Park, Hamstead and Baggeridge. Hamstead now lies outside the county so that, with the closure of Baggeridge Pit in 1969, deep mining in south Staffordshire effectively ended. The emphasis has shifted to open-cast working which continues at Lower Gornal. The south Staffordshire coalfield has left few memorials of its greatness. The collieries that brought fame to places like Bilston, Wednesbury and West Bromwich have quite disappeared. Spoil heaps and the effects of subsidence may mark the sites, as in Lower and Upper Gornal, but the demand for improved living conditions is increasingly creating a new landscape. The parish of Tipton may be cited as typical. When the Tithe Map was produced in 1849 the area was covered with short railway lines linking pits to canals and basins. One concentration of pits was at Puppy Green, but now what one finds is Victoria Park with the ponds created by subsidence replaced by an ornamental lake. The area where small-scale mining continued longest was round Sedgley and Amblecote where the occasional wooden headstocks survive, and this was primarily because of the value of fireclay. One of the Dibdale pits at Lower Gornal was sunk in 1898 and had a horizontal winding engine by Bolton of Swansea that was probably contemporary. A second pit was sunk as recently as 1937–8 and had a second-hand engine built by Thornewill &

Page 89   *Extremes in size:* (above) *Worthington's malthouse and brewery at Hay Walk, Burton-upon-Trent, late nineteenth century;* (below) *the small Delph Brewery, Brierley Hill, Dudley. The present building dates from 1905*

Page 90   *Chatterley-Whitfield Colliery, Stoke-on-Trent:* (above) *general view taken in 1966;* (below) *the Winstanley Pit winding-engine which no longer exists*

Warham of Burton-upon-Trent in 1910. It was closed in 1956. Two relics of fireclay mining are preserved at the County Museum at Shugborough. One is a small winding engine that served pit No 12 of Messrs John Hall & Co of Stourbridge while Amblecote was part of Staffordshire. The second is a wrought-iron barrel of the kind used for drawing water during the sinking of a shaft. It came from Dibdale.

In the north Staffordshire coalfield conditions were altogether different. It is true that coal was apparently being mined as early as in the south—there is a reference to mines at Tunstall in 1282—and no doubt the outcrops and shallow seams were worked in much the same way. But by the early nineteenth century, with the development of deep mining, the frequent faulting and the steep-pitching of the seams meant that each mine or part of a mine had to be treated individually. It was even possible for the seam to incline beyond the vertical so that what was the roof became the floor.

The drainage problem could be met by the cutting of soughs, and the mines belonging to Heathcote & Kinnersley near Chesterton, for instance, were said in the *Staffordshire Advertiser*, 11 November 1809, to be partly 'laid dry by a main gutter about thirty-seven inches high, already completed and two collateral branches'. Nearby in the Goldenhill area the Harecastle tunnel and a cross tunnel 'many hundred yards long' not only drained the mines but provided a means of transport for the iron and coal to the furnace (*Staffordshire Advertiser*, 30 April 1825). But most mines were not so favourably placed, and it was usual to have at least two engines: a whimsey for winding and a 'water-engine' for pumping. Some of the earliest engines in north Staffordshire, as in the south, were supplied by Boulton & Watt. Thus Sir Nigel Gresley bought an 8hp winding-engine for Apedale Colliery in about 1790 at a cost of £40, and in 1792 John Sparrow & Co bought for Cockhead Colliery a 6hp winding-engine and a 100hp pumping-engine. This difference in size between the two types of engine was typical; at Blake Hall Colliery near Cheadle a 9hp winding-engine complemented a 40hp pumping-engine.

F

The pottery industry was far less consuming of coal than the iron-working industries of the Black Country, and in north Staffordshire the emphasis was upon the extraction of ironstone which meant that the greatest expansion came in the early 1870s when a maximum of 3,900,000 tons of coal a year were won. The most impressive early buildings in Stoke-on-Trent were erected as the result of the iron and steel boom. Stafford Colliery, Fenton; Chatterley-Whitfield Colliery, near Tunstall; and Florence Colliery, Longton, all belonged to this period. At the first two, engine houses were suitably monumental, but at Florence there was to be no nonsense, and here the criterion of success was the smallness of expenditure. In 1966 Chatterley-Whitfield retained much of its buildings. Institute Pit, named after the North Staffordshire Institute of Mining Engineers, had a vertical engine house, dated 1875. The second-hand winding-engine of Winstanley Pit was of 20in cylinder and 4ft stroke, with a 10ft diameter drum. Now a winding-engine by Worsley Mesnes of Wigan, dated 1914, is the solitary survivor. Of the remaining seven active collieries of north Staffordshire, all rely on electrical power and are largely modern in other respects. Modern, too, are the licensed mines which, because they are operated by a labour force of less than about forty men, are independent of the National Coal Board. But, although their winding sheds and loading bays are clad in corrugated sheeting, by their very scale the licensed mines evoke something of eighteenth-century conditions. The coal is won by adits not more than about 200yd long. Fourteen such mines were in operation in 1970, predominantly in the Apedale and Red Street areas.

In the last of the three main coalfields, Cannock Chase, coal was being extensively worked at Beaudesert Park from the sixteenth century, and in 1891 it was noted that some of the bell-pits in the park were old enough to have mature oak trees growing on their sides. Essington was one of the first parts of the coalfield to be developed by deep mining. In 1806 the mine at Essington Wood was said to be drained by a very powerful engine, and in that year there was installed a winding-whimsey capable of drawing from a pair of pits, 100 tons of coal per day.

Such pits would have continued as the norm until the 1850s when the pattern suddenly changed, and pits of increasing depth were sunk until the maximum of 1,663ft was reached at Huntington Colliery in 1902. The depth of the pits was matched by the performance of the engines, and although steam has been entirely superseded in Cannock Chase a number of engines that dated from the period of expansion between 1860 and 1900 survived until comparatively recently. At Hayes Colliery, for instance, the 2 cylinder winding-engine, of 24in bore and 5ft stroke, was built by Thornewill & Warham of Burton in 1876; Cannock Chase No 8 Pit had until 1938 a winding-engine by the same firm dated 1867; and at No 7 Pit there was an engine remarkable for the sliding gear that enabled it to be used both for winding and pumping. It may have been by Boulton & Watt. In 1961 there were three steam winding-engines in operation. Cannock Chase No 8 possessed two engines including one dated 1911 by Worsley Mesnes, and Wimblebury had the third which dated from 1927 and was the work of Walker Brothers of Wigan. It must have been one of the last to be installed.

IRONWORKING

Primary processing

The circumstances that affected the history of coalworking in Staffordshire affected that of ironworking also. In the early days the ore was reduced by the bloomery process whereby it was heated with charcoal, hammered out into a slag-free bloom of metal and then shaped by further hammering into bars. A fast-flowing stream and a plentiful supply of timber were required, and so it was that Cannock Chase soon became the centre of the ironworking industry. The reliance on water power was increased after 1561 when William Lord Paget made the revolutionary discovery that larger quantities of ore could be handled in an almost continuous process if blast were injected into the furnace with the aid of water-driven bellows. But now the product was brittle pig-iron or cast iron rather than wrought iron, and in order to arrive at the same result as that of the bloomery process it was necessary to decarburise it in a finery hearth and forge it into bar. It could then be slit into the form of rod. Each of the various processes was undertaken with water power, but they were quite distinct from one another. Whereas it was possible to have the blast furnace near the head of the stream, forges which depended on large quantities of water had to be lower down. Thus Paget's first furnaces, dating from 1561 and 1578 respectively, were near Hednesford and near Teddesley, but the forges and slitting-mill were at Abbots Bromley and Rugeley. Other forges not associated with the Paget furnaces were at Little Aston, Hints, Brewood, Coven, Congreve and Rushall. In the south-west of the county a number of mills were sited on the Stour and Smestow Brook including especially the one established by Richard Foley for slitting iron bar into rods for nail-making. The furnaces and forges were notably lacking where the ore was mainly derived but, so long as water was the source of power, there was no alternative but to carry the ore to lengths of streams that lay beyond the south Staffordshire plateau.

There are still works at Swindon and Cookley (Worcs) but otherwise the ironworking sites of the water-powered phase have long been deserted. The site of Paget's 1561 furnace may, however, be identified at SK 009139 from the remains of the millrace and a heap of slag. The Rising Brook stream is crossed at this point by the approach road to Cannock Chase No 5 Colliery.

The reason for the desertion of the Cannock Chase and other sites was John Wilkinson's application of steam rather than water as the source of power to operate the blowing cylinders. This was in about 1766, but before then the dispensability of charcoal had been demonstrated. In 1621 Dud Dudley, according to the claim published in his *Metallum Martis* of 1665, reduced iron ore with coal; yet even if the claim was justified the contribution had no lasting effect, and it was left to Abraham Darby of Coalbrookdale to introduce coke-smelting. Wilkinson's adoption of the steam-powered blast furnace was immediately followed by two further improvements. One was the use of high quality iron and accurate boring methods to produce the first completely satisfactory steam-engine cylinders. The second was necessitated by the poverty of the Black Country coals in yielding coke. Wilkinson overcame the deficiency by substituting raw coal as fuel and by removing the sulphur content with lime that he obtained from Hay Head, near Walsall. Despite these improvements the output of the new form of furnace was still the traditional brittle pig-iron, and Wilkinson completed his works with a forge and rolling-mill, both served by steam engines. At the same time Henry Cort independently developed the puddling process which was improved by the 'wet puddling' process introduced in 1830 by Joseph Hall of Bloomfield Ironworks, Tipton. At last a satisfactory means of eliminating refining, 'fining' and hammering had been found.

A commemorative plaque has been erected at Bradley near the site of the first Black Country blast furnace, but otherwise the only physical evidence of Wilkinson's activities is the cast-iron pulpit in Bradley Methodist Church and the remains of a slag heap and large quantities of pit spoil. It is therefore fortunate that a painting of the ironworks should have survived at the William Salt Library, Stafford. The main features shown are the square furnace, approached by an incline, two beehive boilers, a large stack and the foundry that covered the fore-hearth and pig-bed. The Wilkinson furnace established a precedent, and by 1791 there were twenty-one blast furnaces in south Staffordshire.

At Springwood, Newcastle, the remains of what is probably a late eighteenth-century blast furnace survive, but in south Staffordshire the great ironworks that gave such distinction to the scene have largely disappeared. The Tipton firm of Horseley & Co, whose name appears on numerous canal bridges, provides a rare instance of continuity. At Wednesbury only two of the eleven ironworks survived the depression of 1875–86, and the Crown Tube Works, with an impressive elevation but in reality a rabbit warren of small shops incapable of supervision, was demolished about 1919. The Cannon Ironworks at Coseley was founded by John Sheldon in 1826, and some of the buildings here, including that surmounted by a bell, are

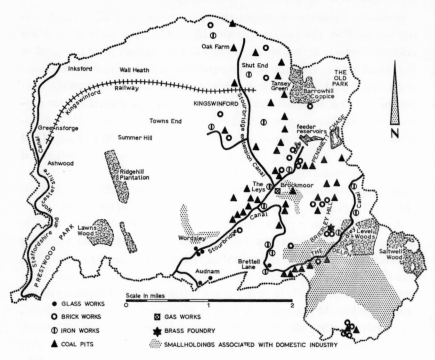

Distribution of industries in Kingswinford Parish. Based on Tithe Map
(1839–40), Crown Copyright reserved

early or mid-nineteenth century. Elsewhere in Coseley, the works of
Thomas Green and Benjamin Parkes, although modernised, retain
something of their early nineteenth-century layout. Generally, however, the ironworks both large and small have gone, but the processes
are recorded in, for instance, copies of sixteen engravings by Chattock
at the William Salt Library, and their former existence may be
evidenced by the present use of the site. This continuity is well illustrated by reference to the Kingswinford Tithe Map where it will be
noted that modern steelworks are often on or near the site of early
ironworks. Because of their use in cooling, the canals are still a factor

determining location. The exhaustion of raw materials, the reluctance to accept the Bessemer steel-making process and a general slump contributed to the fall of the south Staffordshire pig-iron industry. The last puddling forge ceased production in 1960, the New Level Furnaces of the Round Oak Steel works were demolished in 1957, and the only blast furnace remaining, on the site of furnaces erected in 1788, is that of the British Steel Corporation at Bilston. In north Staffordshire the only works in operation is at Shelton.

Secondary processing

The smelting of pig-iron and its conversion into roll and bar had to be conducted on a large scale, but the household objects for which much of the iron was destined were produced in very different circumstances. The work was undertaken by masters who were responsible to factors, with foremen acting as intermediaries. One of the most striking characteristics noted by R. H. Horne for the Children's Employment Commission of 1841 was the intense specialisation within the different areas of the Black Country and its immediate surroundings. For instance, Wolverhampton was the place for locksmiths of whom there were over 260 in 1841. In addition there were 60 to 70 key-makers, the remainder being engaged mainly in making screws, latches, bolts, snuffers, tobacco-boxes and spectacle frames and cases. At Darlaston, Wednesfield and Willenhall the emphasis was also upon locksmiths and key-makers who at Willenhall numbered altogether 344, and because filing was part of the process of manufacture, those who spent their working lives in this way could be recognised by their physical deformity. The right shoulder blade became displaced, and the right leg crooked and bent inwards at the knee, like the letter K. Bilston had 20 to 30 japanners and tinplate workers; Dudley was the centre for glass-making, glass-cutting, vice-making, fire-iron making and chain-making. Wednesbury specialised in gas pipes (previously gun barrels), coach springs and axles, gun-locks and screws; Walsall's associations with leather and saddlery were supported by the manufacture of buckles, spurs and bits; and the most unremunerative of all the industries, nail-making, was primarily reserved for Sedgley, Gornal and Coseley.

Gas pipes and coach springs were produced in factories, but for most other types of article the industry was organised on a strictly domestic basis. At first there may have been only a single workshop in the yard at the back of the house, but as pressures grew the yard became a conglomeration not only of workshops but of dwellings as well. Yet the entrance to the yard through a narrow dark passage that may have also served as a drain remained the same, and one of the difficulties was therefore that of finding a particular master's workshop. Very few of them had a name over the door. Eventually the typical yard contained two to four houses, one or two of which were workshops or contained rooms that were used for this purpose. If the settlement reached larger dimensions it might earn a name such as Pudding Bag or Hellhouse Lane.

Because sewerage and ventilation were not considered necessary in the dwellings built for the working classes, the occupiers of the yard had at best one privy between them, and the only fires in the workshops were those of the hearths. At Willenhall many of the shops were described as 'extremely dirty and dilapidated, sometimes presenting the appearance of little broken sheds. Their floor is generally the earth, a few are boarded, many bricked. They must be wretched places in winter, especially for the feet of all those who stand from day to day at the vice'. But bad as the conditions were in the lock-making area, the palm for squalor belonged to the western borders of the Black Country.

The reason for the squalor lay in the poverty associated with the nail-making industry. This was a light forging operation that lent itself admirably to the domestic system. The factor supplied the master with the bar, and the equipment used was a hearth and a block or cast-iron anvil, carrying a variety of setts or bores in which the nails were formed. Except in the case of small nails, the hammering was done with an object called an oliver. The hammer was brought in contact with the sett by stamping a treadle repeatedly, and when the treadle was released the spring pole that provided part of the linkage shot the hammer up again. Despite the size of the equipment and although room might have to be found for a master and his wife and two children, the great majority of the nail shops measured only about 10ft long × 9ft wide. They were 'filthily dirty' and when not lit presented the appearance of 'a dilapidated coal-hole or little black den'.

Not surprisingly very little is left of the 'hovels' and 'dens' which were numerically the most important of the industrial monuments of south Staffordshire. The drop-stamping forge of Robinson Brothers of Spring Head, Wednesbury (Walsall), is one of the few back-yard workshops still functioning. Another is at the rear of No 46, Newhall Street, Willenhall, where Messrs Edwards & Cook cast brass lock components in a building measuring 24ft × 18ft. At the time of the Tithe Survey in 1844, sixty premises in Sedgley parish could be identified as nail shops, and in 1961 only two of these were still standing. Their association with nail-making had ended even then, and now the only nailer's shop still in regular use, although no longer for the making of nails, is over the county boundary at Mount Street, Halesowen. In Walsall T. Warman & Sons of Eldon Street are the last of the hand-forged bit-makers.

As the traditional industries are abandoned and as the buildings associated with those industries are demolished, it becomes increasingly necessary to study the ironworking areas of Staffordshire in museums and libraries. The museums at Willenhall and Brierley Hill contain representative collections of locks and glass respectively. A Black Country forge, incorporating an oliver and other original equipment may be seen in the Central Museum, St James's Road, Dudley. A nailer's shop has been reconstructed at Birmingham City Museum. Still more important, a Black Country Museum to be sited near the east end of Dudley Canal Tunnel is proposed. Its acquisitions already include parts of Factory Bridge, Tipton, and a rotative beam-engine, of 20in cylinder and 5ft stroke, that came from the Cricket Field works of Price-Pearson Refractories Ltd.

OTHER MINERAL RESOURCES

The remaining mineral resources of Staffordshire are generally related to the building industry, to agriculture and to non-ferrous metals —a classification that should not obscure the fact that some of the resources could be applied to multiple uses. The local sandstone that was used for Staffordshire's industrial and other buildings of the eighteenth and nineteenth centuries came from quarries such as those at Gornal, Hollington and Tixall. Except at Hollington, where the quarries are active, the sites have now to be identified from disturbances in the ground. In the north of the county the sandstone takes the form of millstone grit, and the centre of activity was Mow Cop. The special character is here demonstrated by the housing as much as by the quarries. The houses, inevitably of stone, are barely two storeys high. They are scattered over the hillside, and a compensation for their smallness is the allocation of a plot of land to each. Grindstones were one of the products of the millstone grit; they were also made at Bilston. Grindstones were particularly valued in the Cannock area because of the emphasis on edge-tool manufacture. The works of William Gilpin & Co Ltd at Churchbridge show little obvious evidence of an early nineteenth-century origin, but the diversion of a stream in 1967 led to the discovery of a massive retaining wall composed entirely of discarded grindstones, each 2ft 3in across by 9in deep.

A number of specialist uses was the characteristic also of gypsum. In one form it is alabaster; in another it is the basis of the plaster that covered the floors of malthouses until the 1870s (page 68). Pits in the Tutbury area are evidence of the open-cast methods of extraction that continued well into the nineteenth century. Limestone, like gypsum, has various applications: as a building material, a flux for ironworking and a fertiliser. The abundance of limestone on Caldon Low was the justification for the Caldon Canal, and at Froghall two great series of kilns, one possibly of about 1780 and the other a century later, show where the stone was burnt at the point of transfer from railway to canal. At Rushall in the south of the county, some kilns converted to pigsties are almost all that is left of the Daw End works that supplied limestone to the Black Country. At Dudley the extraction of limestone created the artificial caverns of Wren's Nest and Castle Hill and the quarries that have been adapted as animal pits for the Castle Zoo.

Salt, too, was a fertiliser for the farmer. Until the late nineteenth century the centre of the Staffordshire salt industry was the area round Shirleywich, the village itself being a planned creation of the late seventeenth century. The salt-works, which with their billowing smoke were a feature of the scene in 1838, have long since disappeared except as earthworks, and most of the housing was demolished in the 1960s. At nearby Weston, Earl Talbot established a salt-works in 1820. Designed by James Trubshaw, the result was an impressive two-storey brick building, parts of which survived until 1963. It bore the date '1821' on the pediment and originally contained eight pans. Carriage of the salt and of the coal to evaporate the brine was facilitated by the presence of the Trent & Mersey Canal.

Clay is the material that links the building industry with pottery and ironworking. As with stone, the main evidence, apart from the products, is limited to the pits whence the clay was extracted. Fireclay was mined in both north and south Staffordshire, and the works at The Delph near Dudley were early enough to be shown on the Tithe Map. Fireclay bricks were made there by hand until the 1960s. The keuper marl yielded suitable clay for the making of bricks and tiles in various parts of central Staffordshire, as it did near Hilderstone where Brick-kiln Cottages have a distinctive rat-trap bond as well as a distinctive name. In the Potteries and the Black Country a special firing of the Etruria marl produced the blue engineering bricks that are incorporated in nineteenth-century industrial monuments of Staffordshire and far beyond.

Finally, Staffordshire had valuable resources of copper and lead. On the Weaver Hills, especially at Ribden, shafts mark the sites of workings that were active from before the 1680s to 1862. At Mixon, north of Onecote, more articulate remains include an adit entrance, waste-tips, shafts and shaft-mounds. The mine was drained partly by two waterwheels, and it is possible to trace the three ponds and stream that supplied them. Dale Mine near Warslow was the principal lead mine in Staffordshire; its adit is open and the site of a dressing-floor is recognisable.

Productive as these mines were, the area where activity was most intense and most prolonged was on the opposite side of the River Manifold, at Ecton Hill in the parish of Wetton. Exactly when copper or lead began to be mined at Ecton is uncertain, but a mine already working before the Civil War is reputed to have occasioned the first use of explosives in British mining. The person responsible was probably the Dutchman, Jacob Momma, who had a brass-wire mill at Esher in Surrey. By the time Plot visited Ecton about 1680, mining had been abandoned, but it was subsequently revived and its heyday belongs to the late eighteenth century. The Dukes of Devonshire—the Chatsworth trustees still own most of the mining rights—were chief promoters, and such was their success that in the years 1760–8 Ecton yielded copper worth nearly £57,000. From 1776 to 1817 its value was over £677,000, and the ore was producing 15 per cent copper, compared with 12 per cent in Cornwall. The mines continued until 1889, but by 1871 the yield had fallen to one ton of copper a year.

Only some of the processing of the lead ores extracted from Ecton and elsewhere took place in Staffordshire. Although lead was smelted at Alton, for instance, in the eighteenth century, the smelting was done exclusively in Derbyshire in the nineteenth century. Smelting of copper ore and the working of the metal have played a more substantial part in Staffordshire's industrial history and indeed Froghall brassworks, begun in 1890, flourish today. In addition to small works such as those at Stoke near Stone, the principal centres have been Whiston, Cheadle, Alton and Oakamoor. Whiston in Kingsley parish, significantly near a coalfield, was where the Ecton ore was smelted between 1770 and about 1890. Virtually all that now remains is the slag, whether in the form of waste or used as a building material.

The other centres are linked by the activities of Thomas Patten &

Co who opened a works at Brookhouses south-west of Cheadle in 1719, and another at Alton in Farley parish about 1734. The existing tinplate works that they bought at Oakamoor in 1790 eventually superseded the other two. The main early buildings that were demolished in 1963 were the strip-mill and the rolling-mill. The former, 136ft × 30ft, was of stone and dated 1792. The latter, 68ft × 32ft, dated from 1804 and cost 'upwards of £700'. It was of brick and stone, and an ecclesiastical effect was imparted by the open arcades on either side and the pointed arches that took the place of timber roof-trusses. The whole site is now cleared, but some masonry and the mill-race, besides small items, will be retained and receive due emphasis when Staffordshire County Council's plans to convert the site to a picnic area and landscaped open space have been fulfilled.

CHAPTER SIX

Roads

STAFFORDSHIRE may be considered the crossroads of England. Since medieval, even if not Roman times, the main roads from south-west to north-east and from south-east to north-west have intersected in Staffordshire, so that the communications of the county have long been of national importance. Added to this are the local conditions that have set a premium on the provision of good roads. First, the rich mineral resources—iron ore, coal, salt and clay—could not be adequately exploited so long as the waggons that carried them got stuck in the mud. Secondly, the pottery industry posed its own special problems as soon as salt, clay and flints were imported from outside the county, and as soon as the fragile finished products were destined for a national and overseas market.

TURNPIKES

It is not surprising that Josiah Wedgwood should have been one of the chief protagonists for improved communications and that he was one of the promoters of the turnpike road that was to connect Burslem with the north-bound road at Red Bull, Church Lawton, and with the Uttoxeter road at Newcastle-under-Lyme. In giving evidence before the House of Commons Committee in 1763, Wedgwood was able to say that the existing roads were 'in very bad condition, narrow in some parts, and in the Winter Season impassable in many Places'. There were two ways of taking finished products to Winsford on the navigable Weaver; either direct on pack-horse, or by waggon on a 4½ mile detour through the town of Newcastle. Despite the opposition of the corporation of Newcastle, Wedgwood and his fellow-potters obtained their Act of Parliament in 1763. Henceforward they had direct turnpike access to Winsford and to the navigable Trent at Willington Ferry. By the time of Wedgwood's success the turnpiking of roads throughout the county was gaining momentum. The first Staffordshire road to be the subject of a turnpike act was an 8 mile length from Tittensor through Newcastle to Talke, part of the recognised route from London to Carlisle. The date was 1714. In the south of the county, the roads in the Wednesbury, Sedgley, and Dudley area were poor enough in the 1680s to be singled out for mention by Plot as 'uncessantly worn with the carriage of coal'; much the same was true forty years later when the decay of the Birmingham–Wolverhampton road was attributed to the great number of carriages constantly passing laden with 'Iron and Iron-wares from Wolverhampton, and thereabouts to Birmingham'. In 1726 the Birmingham–Wednesbury road was turnpiked; and in 1729 both ends of the county were linked when the Staffordshire part of the London–Chester road via Canwell, Lichfield, Stone, Darlaston and Woore was also turnpiked. By 1763 all the major towns of Staffordshire were served by turnpike roads.

The result of the establishment of turnpike trusts was not only the improvement of road surfaces but also the reduction in detours and the easing of gradients, on a large or small scale. In particular, a few of the Staffordshire roads carried mail coaches from London, and it mattered to the postal authorities that these should be adequate for their purpose. Because of this national status of these roads it was appropriate that the surveyor to be employed should have been Thomas Telford. On the Ashbourne–Leek road, which carried coaches to Manchester, the trustees did not eventually adopt Telford's plans to avoid Swinscoe Hill, but on the Liverpool road the Talke bypass was built about 1825, and this was followed by the new road between Hanford Bridge and Trentham. Because this substitute for the long steep hill at Hanford encroached on the Duke of Sutherland's estate, the opening in 1836 was performed with exceptional ceremony. Two bugle-players and the Bristol & Manchester mail coach formed part of the procession. It is, however, the Holyhead road with which Telford's name is particularly associated. At Tettenhall, the new deep wide cutting may still be contrasted with the old steep winding hill to the south.

Throughout the county the turnpike trustees were carrying out improvements, and generally these were strictly related to the existing road pattern. But in the Potteries the establishment of new centres of population carried with it the need to create new roads. Thus the Stoke–Milton length of the new road to Leek and the Fenton to Shelton road were both opened in July 1846. The former which passed 'through beautiful scenery' was so level that it could be called a gallop-road along all of its 4 miles. The arrival of the railways in the 1840s soon discouraged further capital investment on turnpikes, but in one area the railway did itself lead to some re-orientation of the roads. This was at Whitmore where the station remained for eleven years the nearest point on the railway to Newcastle and the Potteries. The road from Newcastle was substantially re-aligned between about 1844 and 1846, while a completely new road was opened between Whitmore and Trentham in 1845. By their straightness and easy gradients, these north Staffordshire roads of the 1830s and 1840s, most of them the work of Liddle Elliot, anticipate those of the 1920s and 1930s, the ninety-year gap representing the age of the dominance of the railways.

As more and more Acts were passed, so the number of turnpike trusts multiplied. There were, it is true, some amalgamations—for instance the five trusts serving the neighbourhood of Cheadle were consolidated—but even so, by 1838, forty-seven separate trusts were centred on what was then Staffordshire. In addition there were trusts centred on adjacent counties, but whose sphere of control extended over the Staffordshire border. The trusts varied greatly in importance. In 1838 the most productive of tolls was the Birmingham & Wednesbury trust with a total annual income of £5,478, of which £4,751 was derived from tolls. The surveyor was paid a salary of £150, and the total expenditure was £5,152. The least productive was the Uttoxeter & Callingwood Plain trust which obtained only £76 from tolls and which, like nine other Staffordshire trusts, did not go to the expense of employing a salaried surveyor. During 1838 the turnover of all the forty-seven trusts was about £60,000.

Page 107   *Two Black Country scenes:* (right) *winding gear at Dibdale Colliery, Lower Gornal, Dudley;* (below) *Dial Glassworks, Audnam, Dudley; part dates from the late eighteenth century*

Page 108   *Contrasts in tollhouses:* (above) *Ipstones erected in the 1830s;* (below) *tollhouse in Brick Kiln Lane, Lower Gornal, Dudley*

Tollhouses

The second half of the nineteenth century saw the gradual demise of the turnpike trusts, but for the discerning traveller there are still signs of their former activity. Of these the most obvious is perhaps the toll-house. On the first edition of the Staffordshire Ordnance Survey, dating from 1833 to 1842, about 170 tollgates are shown within the area of the present county. High though it is, even this can be shown not to represent the total number.

Changes in the distribution of the gates usually took place under one of two circumstances. First, a road diversion might result in the bypassing of a tollgate which would therefore need replacement. Thus the tollhouse at Poolhall on the Ashbourne–Leek road was erected in 1828 when the gradient up Lowe Hill was eased. Secondly, it might be necessary to impose closer control over the use of the road. As an illustration of this, the Uttoxeter & Callingwood Plain trustees met in 1831 because the existing gates were found 'entirely insufficient and inadequate to support the credit, good faith, and maintenance of the said road'. Eventually to help meet this problem the existing tollhouse at Highwood Road, Uttoxeter, was erected.

Nearly every tollgate would have been accompanied by a tollhouse, if house is not too grand a term for some of the buildings. The one at Friarswood Road, Newcastle, was small enough to be moved to a new site and converted to a summer-house. That at Bradley Howel is only 10ft square; it probably dates from about 1825, and the single window retains the shelf over which the money and toll-tickets would have passed. Most Staffordshire tollhouses like that in Brick Kiln Lane, Lower Gornal, were, however, large enough to provide living accommodation for the keeper and his family and some, such as those at Dilhorne and Highwood Road, Uttoxeter, are of a size that makes them compare very favourably with contemporary labourers' cottages. Unless existing property could be converted, tollhouses were usually purpose-built, the basic requirements being a room to serve as a ticket-office, windows that allowed a good view of approaching traffic, an

G

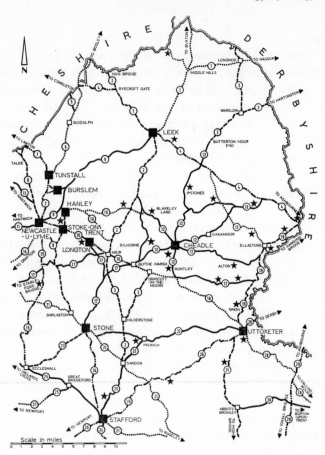

Turnpike roads and tollhouses in north-east Staffordshire. Based on 1in Ordnance Survey maps, first edition (1836–42); House of Commons Accounts and Papers (1840), xlv, pp 22–93; and survey 1966–9

entrance door giving convenient access to the gate, and a board on which to publicise the charges.

Because the requirements were so simple the same design could be repeated with only slight modifications. In 1806 builders were invited to tender for the erection of a tollhouse at Draycott-in-the-Moors; it

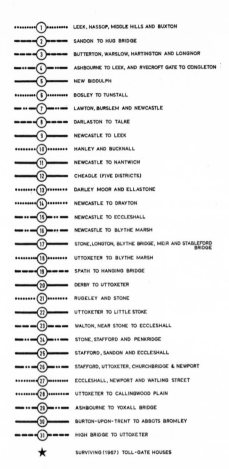

1 LEEK, HASSOP, MIDDLE HILLS AND BUXTON
2 SANDON TO HUG BRIDGE
3 BUTTERTON, WARSLOW, HARTINGTON AND LONGNOR
4 ASHBOURNE TO LEEK, AND RYECROFT GATE TO CONGLETON
5 NEW BIDDULPH
6 BOSLEY TO TUNSTALL
7 LAWTON, BURSLEM AND NEWCASTLE
8 DARLASTON TO TALKE
9 NEWCASTLE TO LEEK
10 HANLEY AND BUCKNALL
11 NEWCASTLE TO NANTWICH
12 CHEADLE (FIVE DISTRICTS)
13 DARLEY MOOR AND ELLASTONE
14 NEWCASTLE TO DRAYTON
15 NEWCASTLE TO ECCLESHALL
16 NEWCASTLE TO BLYTHE MARSH
17 STONE, LONGTON, BLYTHE BRIDGE, MEIR AND STABLEFORD BRIDGE
18 UTTOXETER TO BLYTHE MARSH
19 SPATH TO HANGING BRIDGE
20 DERBY TO UTTOXETER
21 RUGELEY AND STONE
22 UTTOXETER TO LITTLE STOKE
23 WALTON, NEAR STONE TO ECCLESHALL
24 STONE, STAFFORD AND PENKRIDGE
25 STAFFORD, SANDON AND ECCLESHALL
26 STAFFORD, UTTOXETER, CHURCHBRIDGE & NEWPORT
27 ECCLESHALL, NEWPORT AND WATLING STREET
28 UTTOXETER TO CALLINGWOOD PLAIN
29 ASHBOURNE TO YOXALL BRIDGE
30 BURTON-UPON-TRENT TO ABBOTS BROMLEY
31 HIGH BRIDGE TO UTTOXETER
★ SURVIVING (1967) TOLL-GATE HOUSES

Key to map on opposite page

was to be 'according to the model, or upon a plan similar to that of the Toll house near Uttoxeter, upon the Turnpike Road from thence to Stone'. Of surviving tollhouses those near Middle Mayfield and at High Bridge were almost identical originally. Both seem to date from 1828–9; they were erected by two different trusts, but the relationship between these trusts was close enough for them to employ, at least from 1834 onwards, the same clerk and treasurer. These two houses derive their distinctiveness from the recessed entrances at each corner, but the most general concession to ornament was the adoption of Gothic arched windows and intersecting glazing bars. A tollhouse was not an expensive item: the one at Birdsgrove near Mayfield has Gothic windows, it dates from 1842, and the contract price was £95. The now-demolished houses at Greenhill (Cheadle), and Forsbrook cost £67 and £100 in 1836 and 1837 respectively.

Mileposts

If the tollhouse is the most obvious legacy of the turnpike trustees, second position should belong to the milepost. In 1765 the surveyor of the Ashbourne–Leek trust was ordered to erect milestones, and the 'proper inscriptions' that these were to have were no doubt incised direct on the stone. Posts of this description with the name of the township where they are sited and with the distances to places served by the road may be seen between Stafford and Loggerheads on the Woore turnpike.

But as the condition of these posts shows only too well, stone by itself does not provide a durable inscription, and gradually cast iron became more important. At first the post remained stone and the inscription was sunk on a cast-iron plate. The Canwell–Woore trust, which at one time controlled a length of the London to Chester road, favoured this combination of stone and iron. One post is in High Street, Stone; another, re-discovered in 1965, has been set up again at Brereton Road, Rugeley; of three others that have been moved, two are in the grounds of Swinfen Hall and one is in the drive to the site of Manley Hall. Later the lettering, instead of being sunk, tended to be boldly raised. The milestones ordered for the Blythe Marsh to Thorpe road in 1822 were to have cast-iron plates and raised letters, and to the same category belong the post at Upper Gungate, Tamworth, those between Wetley Rocks and Tean and those between Hug Bridge and Sandon. An objection to the form of post with a single face was that it could be read only for the moment when the vehicle or horse was abreast of it. It was better to have a two-faced post with two separate iron plates, and this is the kind erected by the Lichfield–High Bridges trustees and now to be seen near Manor Gardens, King's Bromley, and in the drive to the Old Rectory, Mavesyn Ridware. A much more sophisticated variant occurs 2 miles from Stafford on the road to Stone, where the stone is shaped to receive a single cast-iron casting.

The next logical step was to discard stone altogether, which immediately introduced greater scope for variation. The basic element was often a two-faced post, the top formed by a sloping third face. This is seen between Stourbridge and Bridgnorth, where the signature 'Foster Rastrick & Co Stourbridge' suggests a date of about 1830, and between Woodseaves and Great Bridgeford where the proportions are more squat and the outline irregular. Sometimes a fourth face might rise above the others. The Newcastle–Nantwich, Uttoxeter–Blythe Marsh, and Ashby–Tutbury trusts all adopted this design. A milepost erected by the second of these trusts is signed 'J. & F. Thornewill Burton' and dated '1828'; it is now at the County Museum, Shugborough. The posts of the third trust are signed by Thornewill but undated.

The alternative to the rectilinear design was the one where the potentialities of cast iron were more fully exploited and where the main part of the post was a cylindrical shaft. The distances might be given on two square contiguous panels forming truncated arms—the posts by Sarah Nicklin of Cobridge dated '1821', between Newcastle and Leek, are examples—or the post might swell at the top and the distances be given on the swollen section. 'W.H.' of Derby, William Green of Macclesfield and James Bassett of Ashbourne all produced posts of this design. The first signed a post 2 miles from Burton on the Derby road, the second the set dated '1833' between Leek and Buxton, and the third the equally fine set dated '1834' between Leek and Ashbourne.

When at the end of the nineteenth century the County Council assumed responsibility for most of the county's roads, local idiosyncrasies disappeared.

BRIDGES

Although the chief highway authority is now the County Council, it should not be supposed that this public ownership is entirely a late nineteenth-century development. Even after the establishment of turnpike trusts, the Court of Quarter Sessions continued to be largely responsible for the construction and maintenance of one part of Staffordshire's roads, namely the river bridges whose history in the county is somewhat parallel to that of the mileposts. At the end of the eighteenth century the bridges were generally of stone, like Wolseley Bridge which takes the Liverpool road over the Trent near Colwich. Designed by John Rennie and dating from about 1798, it typifies all that was best in masonry design. It was not until some thirty years later that cast iron was extensively used for two of Staffordshire's bridges: at both Chetwynd Bridge (Alrewas) and High Bridge (Armitage) the principle of construction is the same, and the castings were supplied by the Coalbrookdale Company. Despite the success of these two bridges, cast iron did not altogether replace more traditional materials. The bridge erected at Shirleywich in 1848 and designed by J. R. Remington of Alabama, was of timber; and when Burton Bridge was renewed in 1863–4 thirty of the thirty-two openings were arched with brick and stone, and only the two that crossed railway lines were spanned with iron girders. Burton Bridge, 470ft long, was designed by J. S. Crossley, the engineer of the Midland Railway Company, the same company which, in Mr Langley, produced the man who helped to design probably the only suspension bridge in Staffordshire. This, Ferry Bridge, is also at Burton and takes the Stapenhill footpath across the Trent. Opened in 1889, it is 240ft long and has a centre span of 115ft. The builders were Thornewill & Warham, the Burton engineers and ironfounders, and the identity of the donor, Lord Burton, was profusely acknowledged in the heraldic devices that once adorned the cast-iron casing of the towers.

The tollhouses, the mileposts and the bridges are almost all that is left to remind the traveller of his debt to the turnpike trusts and to the

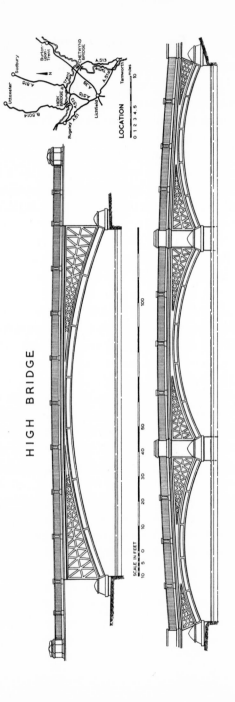

HIGH BRIDGE

CHETWYND BRIDGE

Chetwynd Bridge, Alrewas, and High Bridge, Armitage. Based on drawings (1902) in possession of County Surveyor

Court of Quarter Sessions. The Department of the Environment and the County Council have risen in their place, but despite the changed administration and despite reinforced concrete, Staffordshire is still the crossroads of England. With the idea of a single meeting-point for the country's roads now a reality, the great motorway link lies just within the Staffordshire boundary.

CHAPTER SEVEN

Canals

THE Bridgewater Canal, first of this country's arterial canals, lies outside Staffordshire but the man who designed it was more closely associated with Staffordshire than with any other county. James Brindley moved with his family to the neighbourhood of Leek when he was only ten years old, and it was partly the influence of two Staffordshire men, Earl Gower of Trentham and John Gilbert of Farley, that led to Brindley's introduction to the Duke of Bridgewater. Such was the success of the Bridgewater Canal that those who promoted it turned their attention to something still more ambitious, a waterway link between the rivers Trent and Mersey. It has already been seen how Josiah Wedgwood was anxious to gain easy access to the navigable lengths of the Weaver and Trent and how he succeeded in getting the road from Church Lawton to Burslem and Newcastle-under-Lyme turnpiked for this purpose. He now threw himself wholeheartedly into support for the Trent & Mersey Canal or the Grand Trunk Canal, as it was called by Brindley because of the many branches expected.

So extreme was the optimism that the first branch was authorised in May 1766, on the same day as the main canal. This branch was the Staffordshire & Worcestershire Canal which has, at Compton near Wolverhampton, what is reputed to be Brindley's earliest lock, and at Bratch an embryo staircase of locks. Opened in May 1772, during its creator's lifetime, it runs from Great Haywood to Stourport, and 37 of its 46 miles lie within Staffordshire. The Trent & Mersey Canal itself runs from Preston Brook on the Bridgewater Canal to Derwent Mouth on the navigable River Trent; 49 of the 93 miles are within Staffordshire. In June 1770 the canal was opened from Derwent Mouth as far as Shugborough, and in November 1771 it reached to

117

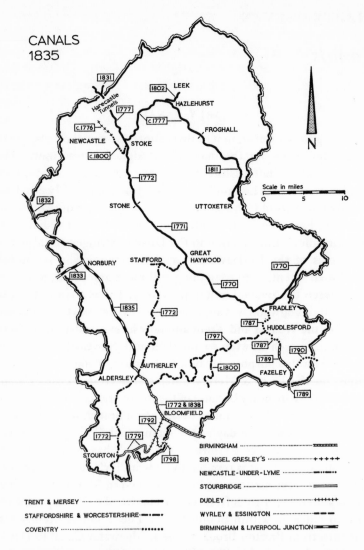

**CANALS
1835**

Caption:
Staffordshire canals. Based on C. Hadfield, *Canals of the West Midlands* and *Canals of the East Midlands* (Newton Abbot, 1966)

Stone. It was not, however, until May 1777 that the whole canal was opened by which time Brindley was dead and his brother-in-law, Hugh Henshall, had succeeded as engineer. The delay in completing this canal was occasioned by the mighty engineering challenge posed by the construction of the 2,880yd long tunnel through Harecastle Hill.

Once Acts had been obtained for the construction of the Trent & Mersey and for the Staffordshire & Worcestershire Canals, steps were soon taken to link Birmingham, Coventry, Oxford and other industrial centres to what was fast becoming a national communications system. For all these extensions, despite their simultaneous construction, Brindley was the engineer. The Birmingham Canal, completed in 1772, runs 23 miles through the heart of the Black Country from Aldersley Junction on the Staffordshire & Worcestershire Canal to Birmingham itself. The number of locks brought with it the problem of maintaining the water level, and this was solved by a formidable collection of pumps powered by steam engines. Of these, Engine No 1 at Rolfe Street, Smethwick, dating from 1777, was one of the earliest to be built by Boulton & Watt. It was moved to the Ocker Hill maintenance depot when it became obsolete and now awaits re-erection at the Birmingham Science Museum. In the south-east, the 32½ mile-long Coventry Canal joins the Oxford Canal at Longford and the Trent & Mersey Canal at Fradley; it is of various dates, but the length from Atherstone to Fazeley was opened in July 1790. At Fazeley it is itself joined by the Birmingham Canal Company's Birmingham & Fazeley Canal that was opened in August 1789. So it was that, by 1790, England was served by a system that linked the navigable waters of the Trent, the Mersey, the Severn and the Thames. The two junctions within this 'Grand Cross', as it eventually came to be known, were at Haywood and Fradley, both in Staffordshire. Thus, even in the canal era, Staffordshire retained its position as the centre of the national communications system.

Once the basic design had been established, it remained to carry out piecemeal extensions. One of the first of the branches was the one that Brindley was surveying when he got soaked to the skin and so precipitated the illness from which he died in 1772. The 17 mile-long Caldon Canal lies entirely within Staffordshire and was completed about 1777. It leaves the summit level of the Trent & Mersey Canal at Etruria and ends at Froghall where it was continued by a tramway that brought down limestone from the Caldon quarries.

Another early branch, completed about 1776, was built by Sir Nigel Gresley between Newcastle and his collieries at Apedale, and it was later connected to the Trent & Mersey Canal by means of the Newcastle Junction Canal, the Newcastle Canal and apparently an inclined plane between these two. In 1802 a branch from the Caldon Canal at Hazlehurst brought the canal to Leek and at the same time had the more important result of serving as part of a feeder from the reservoir at Rudyard Lake, which replenished the Caldon Canal and thereby the main canal. In 1811 an extension of the Caldon Canal reached the town of Uttoxeter, and in 1816 a branch off the Staffordshire & Worcestershire Canal replaced a mile-long tramway as the means of access to Stafford.

Meanwhile, even greater developments were taking place in the south of the county, where numerous branches were built with the aim of shortening distances and giving access to individual collieries. Notable among such branches was the Wyrley & Essington Canal which, when conceived, was to bring the products of the collieries at Wyrley and Essington to the towns of Wolverhampton and Walsall but, as completed in 1797, provided a through link from Wolverhampton to the Coventry Canal at Huddlesford Junction. A branch off the Staffordshire & Worcestershire Canal served the town of Stourbridge and, when this and an extension to Dudley had been completed in 1779, the idea of a further extension to link with the Birmingham Canal at once suggested itself. So the Dudley Tunnel came to be built, and this was followed in 1798 and 1858 by two further tunnels, Lappal and Netherton, all of which pierced the same range of hills. Lappal Tunnel was built to the detriment of the Staffordshire & Worcestershire and Birmingham Canals, and Netherton relieved the congestion on the Dudley Tunnel.

CANAL RAILWAYS

Despite the multiplication of canals throughout the county, differences in level made it impracticable to serve every individual colliery and quarry with its own canal. Resort was therefore had to construction of a tramroad or railway, and such railways, designed for horse-drawn traffic, were the capillaries of the canal system just as much as the canal branches and basins. Some Staffordshire railways, it is true, were internal links from one works to another, and others were orientated towards the roads. But many of the longer railways had the canal as their destination, as at Essington Colliery where there was 'a Rail Road, of between 3,000 and 4,000 yards in length, for conveying the coals to the main line of the Wyrley and Essington Canal Navigation'. Railways are clearly shown on the first edition of the 1in Ordnance Survey and even more so on Teesdale's map of 1832, where a special convention, a representation of a sleepered line, was used to mark them.

Four Staffordshire railways do, however, have more than local importance. One of these is the 3½ mile-long railway that was opened in 1829 and took coal from the Shut End Collieries to the Staffordshire & Worcestershire Canal at Ashwood Basin. Another is the railway that linked Longton and neighbouring potteries and collieries to the Trent & Mersey Canal at Whieldon's Grove. A third is the Consall railway with plate rails, that was over 6 miles long and carried limestone derived from the Caldon quarries to beyond Weston Coyney. The fourth, in fact a succession of four different lines ranging in date from 1777 to 1849, is the Caldon railway which brought limestone from the Caldon quarries to the canal basin at Froghall (Kingsley). Some buildings and the inclined planes of this railway remain.

LATER CANALS

As more and more branches and railways were built the traffic on the main canals increased, and the very success of Brindley's canals was

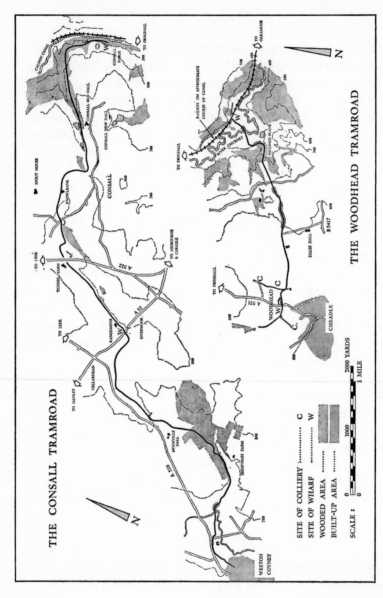

Consall and Woodhead railways. Based on maps in Sale Catalogue (1841) at
Staffordshire Record Office, D952/5/1/30; and J. D. Johnstone, 'The Consall
Plateway', *Railway Magazine*, Jan–Feb (1949), p 15

the cause of their failure. When arterial waterways were a novelty in the second half of the eighteenth century, caution dictated a strict eye on expenditure, and in any case the state of knowledge of engineering techniques imposed limitations. Consequently contours were followed even when tortuous, tunnels were wide enough to take a boat and no more, locks were liberally introduced and rivers, as at Alrewas, might be occasionally crossed on the level. The eventual result was congestion and delay much of the way. The situation was particularly bad on the Birmingham Canal which Thomas Telford was called upon to inspect.

When Telford largely rebuilt Brindley's Birmingham Canal, he reduced the distance between Birminghan and Wolverhampton from 23 miles to 16 miles and the number of locks from 30 to 24. To do this, he abolished the old summit level at Smethwick and replaced it with a cutting 70ft deep, crossed by the Galton Bridge that lies just outside Staffordshire. The canal was now on the 453ft level throughout from Factory Locks, Tipton, to Birmingham. The other main improvement to the Birmingham Canal was that between Bloomfield and Deepfields, where a wide detour was avoided by the building of a 360yd long tunnel at Coseley. With its opening in 1837, the works recommended by Telford were virtually completed.

In the north of the county, the Harecastle Tunnels (Kidsgrove) provide an even better opportunity to contrast the works of Brindley and Telford. The Trent & Mersey Canal Company invited Telford to design a second parallel tunnel, which was begun in 1824 and completed in 1827. At the same time, in order to increase the supply to the summit level, it was necessary to build a new reservoir at Knypersley. This again was Telford's work, and the contractors were Dutton & Buckley.

Both the shortening of the Birmingham Canal and the construction of a second Harecastle Tunnel were localised attempts to improve the canal system bequeathed by Brindley. A much more radical proposal was the Birmingham & Liverpool Junction Canal that ran 39½ miles from the Staffordshire & Worcestershire Canal at Autherley to the

Ellesmere & Chester Canal at Nantwich. It shortened the route from Birmingham to the Mersey by 20 miles and 30 locks and allowed goods to travel from Birmingham to Liverpool in about 45 hours. The price paid for a straight course and maintenance of level was the heaviness and cost of the engineering works. These included Woodseaves Cutting, 1 mile long and up to 90ft deep; Knighton Bank, 1 mile long and 50ft high; Grub Street Cutting, nearly 2 miles long; and finally the cutting and 81yd tunnel at Cowley, near Gnosall. But of all the works the most formidable was the one that could have been avoided had not Lord Anson of Norbury Park refused to allow a passage through his game preserves in Shelmore Wood. Consequently Shelmore Great Bank between Norbury Junction and Gnosall had to be built. Work began in the late summer of 1829, but such were the delays caused by constant slipping of the marl, despite the use of lighter sandy soils, that the bank was still far from complete at the time of Telford's death in 1834. The first boat did not pass along the bank until March 1835.

As to be expected, the difference between the early canals and Telford's is reflected in the scale of the earthworks and in the associated buildings. For instance Brindley's bridges are generally of brick, so that the original ones on the Caldon Canal west of Park Lane can be recognised from their use of this material. Copings are of stone, the brickwork is sinuously curved in both the vertical and the horizontal plane, and a stone label may be added to emphasise the line of the elliptical arch. But otherwise the feature of Brindley's bridges is their diversity, which is to be explained partly by the whims of individual contractors and partly by local circumstances. Sometimes, as at Newcastle Road (Stone), Penkridge, Gailey, Stewponey and Kinver, where an important road crosses over, the towpath was arched separately from the canal itself. The extra strength thus obtained more than compensated for the inconvenience of having to unhitch the horse.

On the Caldon Canal there are six bascule bridges between Ivy House and Oakmeadow Ford, and the same canal has Cherry Eye Bridge, which is of stone and which for some inexplicable reason has a Gothic arch. Two other unusual bridges on Brindley's canals are

Page 125   *The exploitation of cast iron:* (left) *sophisticated milepost, dated 1828, with raised lettering, now in County Museum, Shugborough;* (right) *milepost, dated 1834, still in situ on the Leek–Ashbourne road*

Page 126   *Canal complexities:* (above) *Hazelhurst canal junction, Endon.
The iron-arch bridge, dated 1842, takes the branch towpath over the main
canal; beyond is lock-keeper's cottage;* (below) *Bratch Locks, Wombourne,
on Staffordshire & Worcestershire Canal, opened 1772*

Haywood Bridge (Colwich) at the canal junction and Salt Bridge on the Trent & Mersey. The latter evidently began as an ordinary Brindley bridge but, when the railway was built alongside, the road had to be raised to pass over both canal and railway. At the same time seven orders of brickwork were added to the arch on the south side in order to increase the carriageway width. A final example of an unusual bridge is that for pedestrians near Drayton Bassett. This Birmingham & Fazeley Canal was not in fact engineered by Brindley but belongs to the Brindley tradition. The bridge, which incorporates two brick towers containing spiral staircases, complements the swing bridge for vehicular traffic that lies immediately to the north.

The same austerity that characterises the early bridges is found also in the aqueducts and tunnels. The longest aqueduct, five arches long at Brindley Bank near Rugeley, has been replaced by one of six arches, but the aqueducts of four arches across the Sow and Trent on the Staffordshire & Worcestershire Canal still remain. There is another of two arches across the Stour near Stourton, but the most impressive is that of brick and stone with three arches across the Tame at Tamworth. It was the completion of this in 1790 that allowed the opening of the last of the links of Brindley's system. Of early tunnels, even the longest, Harecastle, has portals that consist simply of a hole set in brick revetting, and their pokiness is usually accentuated by the absence of a towpath. Only the shortest, Dunsley, has a towpath. The one example of an ornamental portal belongs to a tunnel that is some thirty years later. It is at the west end of the Leek Tunnel, where the central feature is a rectangular tablet, but any inscription that it bore is now illegible.

The buildings associated with Telford were as new in concept as were the canals themselves. It is true there was the same avoidance of ostentation, but the relentless way in which the Birmingham & Liverpool Junction Canal or the improved lengths of the Birmingham Canal made direct for their destinations finds architectural expression in the straight lines and carefully engineered curves of the bridges and tunnels. It was important that the progress of road and canal traffic

H

should nowhere be impeded, so that tunnels were made wide enough to incorporate towpaths. On the busy Birmingham Canal at Coseley there are two paths, but one, as at Harecastle and Cowley, was usually enough. On the Birmingham & Liverpool Junction Canal, the scale of the embankments and cuttings may have increased the problem of accommodating the road pattern, but nevertheless the problem was surmounted without compromise. A bridge with semicircular arch and jambs of extraordinary height occurs at The Hollings, Tyrley, and near Norbury a similar bridge, with the addition of a strainer-arch, carries the Newport–Eccleshall road over Grub Street Cutting. Shelmore Great Bank was so immense that it was pierced by tunnels rather than bridges, yet the road remained at full width and semi-circular arches rising from simple square imposts gave adequate headroom. Telford often used stone for facing his bridges, but Staffordshire also contains two fine examples of cast-iron construction. One is Factory Bridge, Tipton, parts of which are now to be re-erected near the Tipton end of the Dudley Canal tunnel as part of the Black Country Museum. The other, near Stretton, takes the Birmingham & Liverpool Junction Canal across the Watling Street and bears Telford's name and the date '1832'.

Differences between Brindley's canals and Telford's appear, too, in the buildings associated with locks, basins and junctions. Whereas the cottages on Brindley's canals show little conformity and may assume such extreme forms as the circular embattled tower near Gailey, Telford's lock-keeper's cottages on the Birmingham & Liverpool Junction Canal and the Newport Branch, whether they be at Tyrley, Wheaton Aston, Norbury or Oulton, follow the same pattern. The cottage is a single-storey structure of brick, with projecting eaves, a central stack, and a door on the left giving access to an octagonal bay. Warehouses, maintenance yards and inns were soon being erected at basins and junctions. In Staffordshire, Haywood, Fradley, Gailey and Stewponey provide good early examples, and on the abandoned Uttoxeter Canal two warehouses were converted to new uses—that at Rocester to a railway warehouse and that at Uttoxeter to a corset factory. Late examples, all on the Birmingham & Liverpool Junction Canal, include Tyrley, where the buildings are dated '1837' and '1840', Norbury and Brewood. A weighbridge platform at Brewood is signed by J. Fieldhouse of Bilston and dated '1841'.

Finally there were two further ways in which concern for the convenience of the canal user showed itself in the early nineteenth century. The first was the erection of cast-iron mileposts that should be both durable and readily legible. They are all of the same design. The second was that the demands of topography and the wish to ease the movement of traffic led to the construction of complicated junctions, anticipating the railway flyovers of the 1880s. The Macclesfield Canal leaves the Trent & Mersey Canal by means of a flyover at Kidsgrove, and so does the Leek Branch of the Caldon Canal at Hazelhurst (Endon). At Bromford Lane, West Bromwich, where there is a link between Telford's Birmingham Canal and its predecessor, the two cast-iron bridges both originated from the Horsley Ironworks, Tipton. The one over the link is dated '1827', and the other '1848'.

The improvements carried out by Telford and his contemporaries reflect how the emphasis on speed had increased since Brindley's day. The trunk railways that would offer speeds to attract passenger traffic were soon to follow.

CHAPTER EIGHT
Railways

THE northernmost point of the broad-gauge system, the major part of Britain's first trunk railway and the headquarters of a railway company that maintained its autonomy until the general amalgamation of 1923 —all these belong to Staffordshire. The same considerations that endowed Staffordshire with importance for the canal engineers commended themselves to their railway counterparts, so that the first trunk railway in the county, the Grand Junction, ran roughly parallel with Telford's Birmingham & Liverpool Junction Canal and likewise was intended to link the two towns that gave the canal its title. More than this it was to link Manchester, for the Liverpool & Manchester Railway had been completed in 1830, and the northern end of the Grand Junction line was at Warrington where there was already a branch from Newton-le-Willows midway between Liverpool and Manchester. The Grand Junction Railway, opened on 4 July 1837, entered Staffordshire at Newton Road near West Bromwich and came no nearer than 1¼ miles to Wolverhampton where it swept northwards and made for Stafford which was the only intermediate town directly served by the new railway. Joseph Locke, the engineer, chose the Whitmore Gap as the crossing-point of the Trent–Mersey watershed. True to form he avoided a tunnel but the sceptics questioned whether the 1 in 180 gradient of the Madeley Incline would prove too steep. It was a triumph for the engineers when a train of four carriages and three laden wagons ascended the incline at a speed of 22½mph.

Birmingham was linked to the industrial areas of Yorkshire by the second of Staffordshire's railways. This, the Birmingham & Derby line, was seen as the centre length of a route that would run from Leeds to London. Opened from Hampton-in-Arden to Derby on

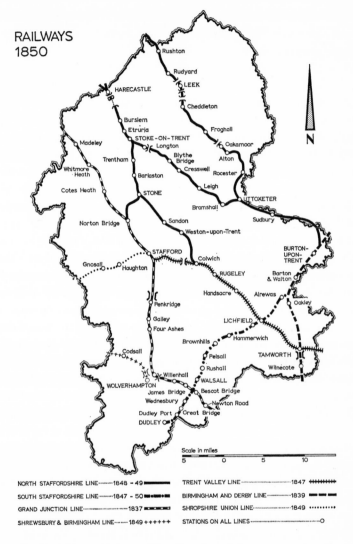

RAILWAYS
1850

Rushton

Rudyard

LEEK

HARECASTLE

Cheddleton

Burslem
Etruria
STOKE-ON-TRENT
Longton

Froghall

Madeley

Oakamoor

Blythe
Bridge

Alton

Trentham

Cresswell

Rocester

Whitmore
Heath

Barlaston

Leigh

Cotes Heath

STONE

UTTOXETER

Bramshall

Norton Bridge

Sandon

Sudbury

Weston-upon-Trent

STAFFORD

Colwich

BURTON-
UPON-
TRENT

Gnosall

Haughton

RUGELEY

Barton
& Walton

Handsacre

Alrewas

Oakley

Penkridge

Galley

LICHFIELD

Four Ashes

Brownhills

Hammerwich

Codsall

Pelsall

TAMWORTH

Willenhall

Rushall

Wilnecote

WOLVERHAMPTON

WALSALL

James Bridge

Bescot Bridge

Wednesbury

Newton Road

Dudley Port

Great Bridge

DUDLEY

Scale in miles

5   O   5   10

N

Staffordshire railways, 1850. Based mainly on reports and
time-tables in *Staffordshire Advertiser*

5 August 1839, the railway was engineered by Robert Stephenson and was important to Staffordshire in that it brought new prosperity to Tamworth and more especially Burton.

After the completion of the Birmingham & Derby Railway, there was a gap of eight years before further railways were opened in the county. For Staffordshire the most important product of the railway mania was the creation, in April 1845, of the North Staffordshire Railway Company, whose projected lines coincided with much of the Trent & Mersey Canal and of its branch to Froghall and Uttoxeter. When later the same year the railway company and the canal company agreed to merge, the result ensured continued viability for the canal, while for the railway it removed potential opposition and facilitated transport of materials in the construction of the lines.

When the first sod of the North Staffordshire Railway was cut on 23 September 1846, it was the inauguration of a whole new network that was being commemorated. It is no wonder that the ceremony was attended with special pomp and festivities. Once these were over, letting of the contracts and construction of the lines proceeded with varying speed, and a network, comprising nearly 112 miles of double track, had been completed by the end of 1849. The total costs incurred by the company amounted to £3,400,000 and were £114,000 less than estimated. The main contract was awarded to Thomas Brassey & Co who, besides a branch to Newcastle, built the lines from Macclesfield to Colwich and from Stone to Norton Bridge. It was this line that partly followed the route of the Trent & Mersey Canal, and the piercing of Harecastle Hill for the third time presented the company with its greatest single engineering challenge. The Uttoxeter–Burton line traversed such level ground that there were only two bridges along the whole route, and the earth for the continuous embankment was obtained by digging canal-like ditches. On the Stoke–Uttoxeter line, let to Price & Leishman, the heaviest engineering works were Meir Tunnel and the viaduct across the town of Longton. Finally on the North Rode–Uttoxeter line, let to Messrs Tredwell, the narrow twisting course of the Churnet Valley imposed the construction of four short tunnels and of viaducts across the river. Construction would have been made much more troublesome were it not that the railway company also owned the Trent & Mersey Canal. As it was, the canal between Froghall and Uttoxeter could be filled in, and the railway was partly laid along its course.

While the North Staffordshire Railway Company was active in the north of the county, the centre was the scene of yet another proposal to shorten the journey-time from London to Lancashire. The original route provided by the Grand Junction and London & Birmingham lines made a detour through Wolverhampton, Birmingham and Coventry. The Trent Valley line, by joining Rugby to Stafford, had the effect of reducing the time by nearly one hour and allowed the commercial traveller from London three hours in Liverpool instead of one and a quarter. Thomas Gooch was the engineer-in-chief, and Mackenzie, Stephenson and Brassey the contractors. The first sod was cut at Tamworth by Sir Robert Peel on 13 November 1845 and the line was opened on 26 June 1847.

The construction of the Trent Valley Railway enhanced the status of Stafford station, and this was further enhanced when in 1849 the Shropshire Union line from Stafford to Shrewsbury was opened.

At Wellington the Shropshire Union line joined the Shrewsbury & Birmingham line which was intended to cover the whole distance between these two places, but in the end the part that would be more expensive to construct became a separate project known as the Birmingham, Wolverhampton & Stour Valley Railway. The line between Wellington and Wolverhampton was opened later in 1849. William Baker was the engineer, and within Staffordshire the major engineering work was the twelve-arch Oxley Viaduct.

The opening of the Shrewsbury–Birmingham line meant that at last Wolverhampton town centre had its own railway station, but there was still no direct link between Wolverhampton and Birmingham, and at the end of 1850 the only line passing through the centre of the Black Country was that of the South Staffordshire Company opened in three stages between 1847 and 1850. The first-class carriages of the company are recorded by the *Staffordshire Advertiser*, 14 April 1849, to have borne panels emblazoned with 'the coat of arms of the borough of Walsall, supported by a representation (on a shield) of Dudley Castle on the left, and the device of the city of Lichfield on the dexter side of the bearing'. Here was recognition of the three towns that were served, and the trains as they rattled over the Gothic bridge at Lichfield or over the viaduct near Wychnor Junction must have been an impressive sight. The third-class passengers were expected to include poor Black Country artisans in pursuit of green fields and fresh air. Thomas Earle was the contractor, and the engineer was the same John Robinson McClean who as engineer of the South Staffordshire Waterworks Company was soon to bring pure Lichfield water to the artisans of the Black Country.

The South Staffordshire line did only a little to link the Black Country with Wolverhampton and London, but during the next few years three lines went far to remedy this situation. The first was the Oxford, Worcester & Wolverhampton Railway, the 'Old Worse and Worse Railway', which was to play so decisive a role in the 'Battle of the Gauges'. When authorised in 1845, it was to be a continuation of the broad gauge from Oxford, but relationships with the Great Western Railway became estranged, and when the whole line including Dudley Tunnel was completed in 1854, narrow gauge was laid almost throughout. The Great Western managed to get mixed gauge substituted, but no broad-gauge train ever ran over the whole of the line, and this remained the position when, as part of the new West Midland, the Oxford, Worcester & Wolverhampton Railway was amalgamated with the Great Western in 1863.

The second line was the Birmingham, Wolverhampton & Stour Valley Railway already mentioned. This was leased to the London & North Western in 1850. Baker & Lee were the engineers, and the contracts were divided between Messrs Branson & Gwyther, Mr Pickering, Mr Hill and Mr Moore. The opening of the line was delayed because the London & North Western were concerned at the implications of a proposed amalgamation between the Shrewsbury

& Birmingham and the Great Western. They wanted to prevent their small rival gaining access to Birmingham and were even prepared to resort to force. The scene at Wolverhampton High Level station when a London & North Western engine, *Swift*, with its brakes tightly screwed down, obstructed a Shrewsbury & Birmingham train was one of the most spectacular in English railway history. Thanks to such tactics it was not until 1852 that the line was opened.

Faced with the inability to make joint use of the Stour Valley line, the Great Western Railway built the third of the lines that crossed the Black Country: engineered by John Robinson McClean, it passed through West Bromwich, Wednesbury and Bilston and was opened in 1854. Like the Oxford & Birmingham Railway it was of mixed gauge. Even after completion of the lines, Wolverhampton continued to be frontier territory. One condition under which the Shrewsbury & Chester and Shrewsbury & Birmingham railways were amalgamated with the Great Western in 1854 was that they should never be converted to broad gauge. For the first time the Great Western found themselves owners of both narrow- and broad-gauge metals which at once introduced the burden of building and maintaining two sets of locomotives. As the two Shrewsbury railways had established a joint locomotive shop at Stafford Road, Wolverhampton, in 1853, it was natural that Wolverhampton should become the headquarters of the narrow-gauge division of the railway.

By the end of the 1850s the basic structure of Staffordshire's railway system had been completed. The London & North Western Railway which had been formed in 1846 mainly from the Grand Junction Railway and the London & Birmingham (the latter including the Trent Valley), took a lease of the Shropshire Union Railway in 1847 and then absorbed the South Staffordshire Railway in 1867. The Midland Railway absorbed the Birmingham & Derby Railway in 1844, and in 1879 it acquired independent access to the Black Country by the opening of the Wolverhampton Walsall & Midland Junction Railway. In 1881 there came a new contestant to the Staffordshire scene in the form of the Great Northern Railway who, by acquiring the locally built and independent Stafford & Uttoxeter Railway opened in 1867, achieved the westernmost limit of their territory. The line was one that ran across difficult terrain. A deep cutting had to be excavated at Hopton, the greatest gradient was as much as 1 in 70, and Loxley Tunnel extended 320yd. In the north of the county, the North Staffordshire Railway opened in 1852 a branch from Rocester to Ashbourne. And the famous and remunerative 6 mile loop line, serving Cobridge, Burslem, Tunstall and Goldenhill, was completed in 1875.

It was the same railway company who, in 1904, began working one of the earliest of the narrow-gauge railways constructed under the Light Railways Act of 1896. This was the Leek & Manifold Valley Light Railway. A standard-gauge line from Leekbrook near Leek connected at Waterhouses with the 2ft 6in gauge line that, passing near the moorland villages of Grindon, Wetton, Butterton and Warslow, had its terminus at Hulme End. The minimum curve on the main Manifold line was 4 chains in radius, and the maximum gradient was 1 in 41. The single tunnel at Swainsley was 154yd long. Such a railway is a far cry from the Grand Junction line where a 1 in 180 gradient was regarded as steep and which scarcely attempted to serve places of less importance than Birmingham, Liverpool and Manchester.

STATIONS

The concept of the function of the stations changed almost as quickly as that of the lines themselves. The earliest surviving station in the county until 1970 was probably that, measuring 32ft × 14ft, at Norton Bridge; it consisted merely of three interconnecting rooms under a slated hipped roof and no doubt typified the conditions under which those who first patronised the Grand Junction Railway waited for trains. The stations of the Birmingham & Derby line are not known to have been any different.

Soon, however, it became apparent that intermediate stations must be better equipped, and the early companies paid for their parsimony by having to pull down their railway stations and build new ones. In these later buildings the essential elements on the ground floor were a booking hall, two first-class waiting-rooms for each of the sexes, some scanty second-class accommodation and nothing but the right to use the trains for third-class passengers. On the upper floor were rooms for the stationmaster, or for the porters and waiting-women. At Walsall there was only an 'ample' platform for south-bound passengers, but at most larger stations the public facilities were duplicated on each side of the track. At Stoke even the road approaches were duplicated, but such attention to safety and convenience was exceptional: walking across the track was normal, and on the Great Western Railway between Birmingham and Wolverhampton the bridges that connected the two sides of a station were rare enough to be specially noted. Finally it was important to protect passengers from the weather both as they entered the booking hall and as they boarded the trains. At smaller stations a porch might suffice, but at larger ones, such as Stoke, Stone, Leek and Walsall, a portico gave access to the booking hall and first-class waiting-rooms.

The improvement of railway stations inevitably increased considerably the cost of their erection. On the Trent Valley Railway the stations averaged 5 miles apart and their cost worked out at £1,720 per mile. The corresponding North Staffordshire figures were 4 miles and £1,300. There were some shareholders who severely criticised the cost of the North Staffordshire stations. Cheddleton and Oakamoor in particular were cited as being disproportionate to the company's requirements, but the main censure was reserved for Stoke station which largely owed its size to the inclusion of a splendid board-room and of flanking offices for the administration of the railway and canal respectively. Its cost was about £30,000.

Not only were the Staffordshire stations of the mid-nineteenth century more commodious and expensive than their predecessors but they were also designed by professional architects. John Livock of London was employed by the Trent Valley, and Edward Adams of Westminster by the South Staffordshire. H. A. Hunt, also of Westminster, designed the North Staffordshire stations of Stoke and Stone, while it was the opportunity to superintend the erection of the Churnet Valley stations that brought William Sugden to Staffordshire in 1848 and so introduced to Leek an architect who, more than any other, was to leave his mark on that town's appearance.

Livock and his contemporaries were keen to give each station an individual character and to win the kind of comment accorded to the Trent Valley stations by the *Staffordshire Advertiser*, of 8 May 1847: 'A great diversity of style is perceptible . . . and a total absence of that monotony . . . observable on most lines'. If temporary stations be ignored—Gnosall's was described by the *Staffordshire Advertiser*, 2 June 1849, as 'a paltry wooden hut, in which the clerk and a passenger would find it difficult to exchange a ticket for money without jostling each other'—there was a choice of four basic styles.

First the station could be 'modern'. Longton station was thus described in 1848, and no doubt a severe blue-brick and stone façade was reckoned suitable for a town that was itself so largely a product of the Industrial Revolution. The stations at West Bromwich, Wednesbury and Bilston 'which harmonise well with the district' should also be included in this category. Far from being of different styles, they are identical with one another and observe a rugged adherence to the functional tradition.

The second style was the Italianate one. Stafford station, rebuilt 1861–2, was described with little justification as being of 'an Italian character'. So, too, was High Level station, Wolverhampton, completed in 1850. The building still stands at the corner of Railway Street and Horseley Fields; the elaborate Tuscan façade in brick and stone has blocked archways and is surmounted by two turrets containing a clock and a wind-dial respectively. In most rural settings an Italianate station might have seemed incongruous, and in any case there was the problem of what to do with the vertical emphasis that the style required. In Staffordshire a truly Italianate style was adopted for two country stations, on each occasion because of the nearness of a landed estate. At Alton (Farley) the station served Alton Towers, the seat of the Earl of Shrewsbury. At Trentham the station was not only designed to match Trentham Hall, the seat of the Duke of Sutherland, but was even the work of the same architect, none other than Charles Barry.

The third style was the half-timbered one, still being practised in 1881 when Burton station began to be rebuilt. The style was then described as 'early English'. Perhaps the best example of a half-timbered station in Staffordshire was Rugeley on the Trent Valley line. In its original form the ground floor was of stone, and the upper part was plastered and half-timbered 'similar in general effect to the old manor houses that so much abound in Shropshire and Cheshire'. The North Staffordshire was another company that sometimes resorted to half-timbered stations.

The fourth choice of style, the predominant one, was the Jacobean, or, as it was often called at the time, the Elizabethan. Such a style, enlivened with mullioned windows, oriel windows, shaped gables, clustered stacks and scalloped roof-tiles, was homely and traditional, two qualities that might be expected to appeal to that small section of the public which travelled regularly. Tradition was sometimes emphasised by heraldry, as at Lichfield Trent Valley where the shield was slotted to receive a lance. At Blythe Bridge and Weston-upon-Trent, the single-storey porches were a rare instance of repetition of the same design, and each carried a plain shield. In deference to local conditions, the Churnet Valley stations, like those at Cheddleton and Froghall are mostly of stone whereas those on other North Staffordshire lines tend to be of red brick decorated with chevron patterns in blue brick. Regardless of the main building material, a distinguishing feature of North Staffordshire stations are the canopies. At Blythe Bridge the cast-iron columns are decorated with Jacobean strapwork, and where the brackets, as at Stone, are of cast iron, the spandrels are characteristically filled with a six-pointed star within a circle. Of rural stations three call for special mention. Colwich has its date '1847' inscribed on a decorative scroll. Sandon has a porte cochère to receive the Earl of Harrowby's carriage, and

Rugeley and Tamworth railway stations; Shugborough railway tunnel. From
Illustrated London News of 4 December 1847

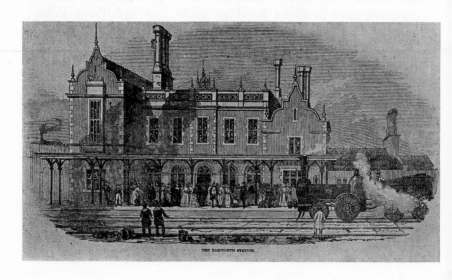

Oakamoor looked Gothic enough to explain its very questionable attribution to that champion of Gothic architecture, A. W. N. Pugin.

OTHER RAILWAY BUILDINGS

Despite the trouble that was taken over the appearance and furnishings of stations, whatever their style, one amenity omitted from all but the largest was a refreshment-room, so that, without dining-cars, passengers went hungry or fed on sandwiches. The inadequacy of the second Stafford station in this respect was soon noted, and in 1849 an effort was made to meet the situation. Although the new refreshment-rooms were only temporary wooden structures, they were successful enough to be described by Charles Dickens as 'a vortex of dissipation compared with the extinct town-inn, the Dodo, in the dull High Street'. Indeed, the congestion was enough to show that more accommodation was sorely needed. In 1859 a new dining-room, 40ft long × 20ft wide, was erected at Stafford.

Another need of the railway passenger was a bed for the night, and one of the most notable features at Stoke was the North Stafford Hotel which was designed by the same architect as was the station, the one being intended both scenically and functionally to complement the other. This combination of station and hotel is unquestionably the finest piece of railway townscape in the county. The North Staffordshire Railway also had the Churnet Valley Hotel at Leek and the Cliffe Park Hotel near Rudyard Lake, and indeed most of the more important stations were accompanied by hotels or inns, even if these were not necessarily managed by the railway company. Rural examples are found at Rushton where the Railway Inn had been opened by 1860, and at Hulme End where Ralph Bassett renamed his premises the Light Railway Inn. At Wolverhampton, where the first station was at Wednesfield Heath, a hotel nearby was being built in 1843 to the design of the London architects, Wyatt & Brandon, who were also responsible for Tixall church, near Stafford.

Railway engines no less than the passengers had to have their

place for rest and resuscitation. Some early engine houses were
circular. That at Stoke, another of the designs of H. A. Hunt, was
one of these. With the aid of a central turntable, engines could be
driven into any one of twenty-four 'stalls'. The engine house should
be linked in the imagination with the 0–6–2 tank locomotive, re-
painted in its original North Staffordshire livery, which is one of the
railway exhibits at the County Museum at Shugborough.

The stations and hotels gave the railway companies their best
opportunity to display architectual dexterity, but lesser buildings
were not altogether neglected, and level-crossing lodges lent themselves particularly to the Jacobean style. The *Staffordshire Advertiser*
could say of part of the North Staffordshire railway in April 1848 that
'comfortable lodges, of the same architectural character as the stations,
are in course of erection at the level crossings', and indeed most of the
lodges built by this company are miniature versions of the railway
stations. Occasionally a large two-storey building, as at Caverswall
Lane, Meir, occurs, but generally the buildings are single-storey with
perhaps the addition of a triangular, square or octagonal bay that
commands a view in both directions of the railway. The lodges are
usually of brick, but at Newton near Cresswell and at Oakamoor they
are half-timbered like the stations at Denstone and Rudyard.

The multiplicity of crossing lodges is an acknowledgement of the
level terrain over which most of the earlier railways pass. No tunnels
apart from Harecastle, Dudley and Meir are more than 800yd long,
but of the others two stand out, if only because their entrances are
extreme examples of self-disguise. At Leek the tunnel pretends to be
a natural cavern in the rock. At Shugborough (Colwich), one entrance
hints of an Egyptian temple and the other of a Norman castle.

The engineers may have succeeded in avoiding tunnels, but the
penalty for following the valleys was the number of roads, rivers and
canals that had to be crossed. Joseph Locke's bridges on the Grand
Junction line are sturdy structures of brick and stone. North of
Stafford the line was quadrupled by 1876, but on the less-used length
between Stafford and Wolverhampton the original bridges over the

Page 143   *Communications through landed estates:* (above) *bridge of about 1832 over Shropshire Union Canal, Chillington Hall, Brewood;* (below) *Trent Valley Railway bridge over Lichfield Drive, Shugborough, Colwich. The line was opened 1847*

Page 144
Jacobean-style grandeur of Stoke-on-Trent railway station. Opened 1848, this was the headquarters of the North Staffordshire Railway

line remained remarkably intact until electrification led to their virtual obliteration. Their style remains illustrated by Penkridge Viaduct, the earliest of Thomas Brassey's railway contracts and the most formidable engineering work along the Staffordshire part of the line. The Birmingham & Derby Railway produced two notable viaducts both of which lay in Staffordshire: the one at Tamworth was of stone and cost £17,625; the other, near Wychnor, was of timber and crossed the Trent and Tame at their confluence. This second viaduct, 1,286ft long with 20ft openings, was supported on 1,000 piles driven 15ft below the river beds. It was constructed by Messrs Jackson & Bean for £15,944.

Wychnor Viaduct has long since ceased to be of timber, and its history is similar therefore to that of many other Staffordshire viaducts. At one time timber was in fact extensively used. On the Churnet Valley line a bridge of 'wood gearing', 120ft long, took the railway over the river near Oakamoor, and beside Leek station the bridge that carried the Newcastle turnpike road was of Sandwich girder design. The name was derived from the bolting of an iron plate between a pair of balks sawn down the middle. Gradually, however, timber was replaced, by wrought iron and later by steel.

Of iron bridges an early Staffordshire example is that at Codsall signed by Thomas Perry & Son of the Highfields Foundry and dated 1848. Some bridges were of compound trussed-girder design and consisted of a straight cast-iron beam strengthened by a truss of wrought-iron tie rods. And then came the disaster of May 1847, when a train plunged into the Dee from a bridge of this construction near Chester. At this date the Trent Valley line was nearing completion, and it would have been too late to alter the four Staffordshire bridges with compound girders. The government inspector gave them special attention and decided that all, including one of 70ft span near Tamworth, were satisfactory.

The Dee Bridge disaster spelt the end of the use of cast iron, and the new model to follow was Stephenson's tubular Britannia Bridge across the Menai Strait. Even before the Britannia Bridge was

I

opened, at least two North Staffordshire bridges, those at Longton
and over the Trent & Mersey Canal near Stoke, had been built upon
the same principle. When Longton Bridge was rebuilt in 1889,
wrought iron was still used, but this time bowstring girders were
substituted. G. J. Crosbie-Dawson, the North Staffordshire engineer,
was the designer both of the new Longton Bridge and of a similar
one at Norbury, dated 1906.

CLOSURE

The competition of the internal combustion engine has made the
railway history of Staffordshire palindromic. The latest railways are
the ones that, on the whole, were closed first. Whereas the Manifold
narrow-gauge railway was closed in 1934, the Grand Junction line, the
Trent Valley line and the main North Staffordshire line have all been
thought viable enough for electrification. The retrenchment has been
accompanied by the search for a new image—a search that contrasts
strangely with the affectation of antiqueness assumed by the railways
when they were genuinely new.

PART TWO

Gazetteer

THE aim has been to include here all those sites considered by reason of interest and condition to be the most important and representative industrial monuments in the geographical county of Stafford. Where monuments receive a reference in Part One but not in the Gazetteer it is usually because they have been destroyed with little or no trace. The method of selection has resulted in the omission of repetitive items such as mileposts and of areas whose interest is mainly derived from the total environment. The canal basin in the centre of Walsall and the shoe-making area of Stafford fall within that category. Entries are arranged topographically according to local authority areas except that parishes are used in the case of rural districts. The boundaries throughout are those effective in 1973. All the sites (except the underground workings at Ecton!) have been seen by the author, and the visits were mostly made and completed between 1966 and 1969. Such has been the rate of destruction that some descriptions will be out-of-date, but the incorporation of the more significant changes that took place before the end of 1973 has been attempted. Finally it should be stressed that many of the industrial monuments appearing in the gazetteer are private property and that the rights of ownership should be respected.

ALREWAS

Bridge (SK 188139). At Chetwynd Bridge, three arches, the centre one of 75ft span, take the Alrewas–Tamworth road across the River Tame. Formerly Salter's Bridge but renamed after Sir George Chetwynd Bart, Chairman of Quarter Sessions, its inscriptions record the County Surveyor as Joseph Potter and the date as 1824. A fine example of cast-iron engineering, each arch consists of five ribs

149

carrying lattice-work over which is the deck. Each rib consists of five castings held to one another and to the cross-bracing by techniques clearly derived from carpentry. Mitre joints are used for the outside ribs, and tenon and mortice joints for the inside ones. The whole is then bolted together.

The ironwork was supplied for £2,918 by the Coalbrookdale Company, and 1824–7 Thomas Webster was paid £2,851 for the masonry of the piers and abutments (see also page 151).

Canal junction (SK 140140). The canal from Fradley to Whittington Brook, completed 1787, is part of the Coventry Canal and here, at Fradley, it joins the Trent & Mersey Canal. As the junction lay in isolated heathland, buildings to meet the needs of men, boats and horses had to be specially provided, and some of those that survive probably date from soon after 1787. Pre-eminent is the two-storey brick range, distinguished with a pediment, directly opposite the junction.

Like Norbury (qv), Fradley is the site of a British Waterways Board maintenance yard, serving the length to Huddlesford Junction and those from Burton to Trentham and Gailey. The buildings are some distance east of the junction on the south side of the Trent & Mersey Canal and were formerly reached on land only by a footpath. The main range dates from 1872.

ALSTONFIELD

Mill (SK 145551). Lode Mill, a two-storey stone and tiled building served by a leat off the River Dove, contains a corn-grinding mill and kiln. The level-breast wheel, 14ft × 5ft 6in, is of iron apart from the two sets of six wooden arms; it is signed by John Edwards who flourished as a millwright at Congleton in 1850.

ALTON

Smelting mill (SK 060432). In 1741 it was described as 'new Erected'; by 1760, £504 had been expended and the site comprised 'a certain Smelting Mill, Refinery, Slag Harth, Smiths Shop, two

Houses, a Barn and about Nine Acres of Land lying near the same with a Pool of Water'. Shareholders after 1760 included the Duke of Devonshire and were the same as those of certain mines at Ecton 'likely to produce large Quantitys of Lead Oar' (p 203).

By 1786 the smelting mill was a corn-grinding mill, a use evidenced by existing remains. There is a single high-breast waterwheel, 20ft × 3ft 4in. There were two sets of eight wooden arms, but only one is intact; otherwise only the iron shaft and iron shrouds survive. The other machinery, including sack-hoist, is in a stone two-storey building at the centre of the complex and approached through a doorway with 'I.S. 1789' scrawled on the right impost. The floors have been removed, and the complete sequence of machinery can be seen in one view. The usual system of gearing drove three pairs of stones, in position except for one runner.

ARMITAGE

Bridge (SK 092167). High Bridge, Armitage/Mavesyn Ridware, of cast iron and crossing the River Trent in a single 140ft span, supersedes the stone bridges that lay slightly downstream. Designed by Joseph Potter, the Coalbrookdale Company supplied the ironwork at a cost of £3,782 (cf Chetwynd Bridge, p 150). The parapets of both bridges with their solid panels and scroll-ornamented posts were cast from the same mould, but High Bridge because of its greater span is more elaborate. There are seven, not five, castings to each rib, a single system of diagonal bracing supplements the cross-bracing, and cross-struts add rigidity to the lattice-work. The masonry of the abutments was provided for £3,005 by William Frith. The date on the inscription panels is 1830.

AUDLEY

Mill (SJ 775501). Boughey's Mill is one of three Staffordshire mills where corn grinding is still performed by water. The miller is Mr Frank Hodgkins, and the product is primarily poultry-feed. The overshot wheel, 15ft × 4ft 2in, entirely of iron and with eight arms, drove two pairs of stones, but these were removed about 1936 when modern machinery driven by countershaft off the crown-wheel was installed. The pit-wheel is signed by C(hristopher) Kirk of Etruria.

BASWICH

Pumping station (SJ 975213). Belonging to Stafford Corporation, the building fronting the road at Milford pumping station is an extension opened on 12 April 1912. Although a new electric plant has been built nearby, the steam engine by Combe Barbour of Belfast survives—a triple-expansion vertical condensing engine with 3-throw plunger pumps. At 30rpm it raised 1,400gal per min. The stroke is 2ft 6in, the three cylinders 14in, 23in and 36in diameter. The original engine house to the south-east was opened on 17 March 1890, and contained two horizontal condensing engines with double-acting pumps by J. Warner & Sons, London.

BETLEY

Farm waterwheel and buildings (SJ 751490). The wheel at Betley Hall Farm served only the needs of the farm. High-breast, and of cast iron, it has a toothed ring on the side of the rim; 16ft × 5ft 1½in, there are eight arms and it drives two pinions. It also drove through the shaft a chopper and a pair of stones that still exist in the room above the dairy. Presumably dating from about 1840, the wheel has been out of use since about 1920. The building that contains it seems to be contemporary, and is part of a large brick and tiled complex of as much interest as the wheel itself.

Because of the slope of the ground, the upper floors of the east and west ranges are at ground-floor level in relation to their east sides. The east range has shippons on the upper floor and loose boxes on the ground floor but, in the west range, the uses are reversed. The lower floors of both ranges are vaulted in brickwork.

BREWOOD

Bridge (SJ 888075). Chillington Hall is approached from the east by a 2 mile avenue of oaks and, where the Shropshire Union Canal passes obliquely under the eastern part of the avenue, the most ornamental canal bridge surviving in the county was constructed. The semicircular-headed arch is set in rustic masonry, the whole surmounted by a corbelled cornice and classical balustrade. As much as 40ft wide between the parapets, the curvature and length of the sweeps was determined by the skew construction and the need to align the ends of the sweeps with both the avenue trees and the top of the cutting.

BROWN EDGE

Mill (SJ 895547). The construction of Knypersley Reservoir, authorised by Act of 1823, necessitated rebuilding Knypersley Mill. The Trent & Mersey Canal Company evidently built the mill themselves, which explains the unfamiliar design and attention to detail. The tablet on the south-west elevation inscribed 'ERECTED, A.D. 1827', and the segmental-headed openings, make the mill reminiscent of, eg, the Red Bull and Pool Lock aqueducts (p 172).

The mill is fed by a tree-lined pool; the high-breast wheel, 16ft × 4ft 1in, has ten wooden arms, wooden sole-boards and buckets. The conventional gearing survives, also the remains of four pairs of stones. The wheel's maker may have been John Cope of Milton near Burslem, who in February 1827 offered for sale the wheel of the about to be superseded Knypersley Mill.

BURSLEM, see STOKE-ON-TRENT.

BURTON-UPON-TRENT

Albion Brewery (SK 231233). Designed by W. & S. T. Martin of Nottingham, this brewery was erected in Shobnall Road in 1875 for the London-based Mann, Crossman & Paulin who in 1902 sold it to J. Marston Thompson & Son Ltd. The brewery proper stands at the centre of the site—an impressive red-brick building—the semicircular-headed panels all round make the exterior unusually uniform.

It overshadows the cooperage (now the engineer's shops) at the north-west corner of the site, and the stables (now stores) along Crossman Street. On the rest of the 82 acre estate, Mann, Crossman & Paulin built a model village, lining Shobnall Road with workmen's cottages, foremen's houses, a hotel and a church, and using Shobnall Grange as the manager's house.

Bass Breweries (SK). Bass's first brewery began, like so many others at Burton, as the adjunct to a town house. The house, bought in 1777, is now 136 High Street, and its grounds extended towards the River Trent, the Hay Ditch providing the necessary drainage.

The Old Brewery as it was still called despite reconstruction in 1884–5, was demolished in 1971; the only other buildings to remain in this part of the town are the Tudor-style offices of about 1880, and the 120ft high tower, complete with 60,000gal tank, of 1866.

In the mid-nineteenth century Bass began expanding from their original site. The Middle Brewery (247232) was built in 1853. The brewhouse was demolished in 1960, since when the fermenting buildings have been adapted for chilling and conditioning plant. The engineer's office and the ale and hop stores, with a storage area of over 5 acres are of about 1853 and 1865 respectively. In the yard to the north, at 249234, the three-storey joiners' shop dates from 1866. In Middle Yard, between Guild Street and High Street, the Electric Cooperage, formerly the Steam Cooperage (249230), was built in 1864; two of its machines are now at the Museum in Shugborough.

New Brewery, now Bass No 2 Brewery, at 246230 on the opposite corner of Station Street and Guild Street, started production in 1864 and is now the oldest of Bass's Burton breweries. The two shortened stacks are each dated 1863.

In Wetmore Road (252236), on the west side of what was Anderstaff Lane, six malthouses run parallel to one another. Nos 16 and 17 at the north end comprise a single range, three storeys high, inscribed 'ERECTED 1863'. The barley intake is at the centre, and the production proceeds thence to the opposite ends of the range. Nos 18–21, inscribed 'ERECTED 1864', are separate houses with the barley store over the top of the working floors. The building to the west of malt-house No 18 is an empty engine house. Floor malting continued here until about 1965.

In 1887 the range of maltings at Shobnall (234229) was said to be the largest in the world belonging to any one firm. Nos 1, 2, 3 and 4 are 1873; Nos 5 and 6 are 1874; and No 7 is 1875. All are four storeys high, designed by William Canning, the company's chief engineer, at a total cost of nearly £100,000. To the south an eighth malthouse designed by Herbert Couchman, has compound riveted steel joists and was added in 1891. Nos 4 and 5 malthouses are separated by a pumping station, and there is a second station beside No 8.

Despite wide-flung distribution, a common architectural treatment, substantial construction and high standard of craftsmanship unify the buildings erected by Bass in the second half of the nineteenth century. Externally, red-brick walls are relieved by semi-circular-headed panels linked at springing-level by a stone string-course. Internally, there is a partiality for queen-post roof trusses and much use of deal supplied by William Bass, timber merchant and brother of Michael Thomas Bass, the brewer.

Clarence Street Brewery (SK 241225). A stone tablet, reset in what used to be the racking-room, records that this brewery was erected by the trustees of the late Peter Walker in 1883, with Scamell & Collyer of London as architects. The brewery itself ceased to be used as such about 1925, and has since been reduced in size and substantially altered internally. The maltings were not converted to grain stores until 1967 and still possess some unusual features.

The striking oddity is the octagonal kiln, surmounted by a goat-shaped copper vane, at the Clarence Street end of the northern malthouse. Circular inside originally, it was the only one of this shape noted by Alfred Barnard in 1887. The shape was determined by the use of steam-driven prongs and brushes for turning the malt. The 5hp steam engine has been removed from alongside the kiln.

Mill (SK 262240). A watermill at Winshill is mentioned in the Domesday Survey and 'Burton Flour Mills' still exist, although the waterwheel was superseded in the 1930s by two turbines. The brick and stone three-storey mill, nucleus of the present complex, bears a tablet dated 1745, but most of its windows have cast-iron frames and are renewals. A Royal Exchange firemark beside the date tablet relates to a policy of 1792 under which Joseph Wilson, miller, insured his utensils and trade for £500. The four-storey northern extension dates from 1889.

South-west of the mill, a four-storey brick building that for part of its life was a mill and is now a store. It has iron-framed windows, marks indicating a level-breast waterwheel, and timber floors and roof subsequently reinforced with cast iron. The building's origins are learnt from a Sun Insurance firemark and a policy register showing that, in 1781, Robert Peel of Burton-upon-Trent and William Yates of Manchester were among six cotton manufacturers who insured their brick and slated warehouse for £600 and its contents for £1,200. The building thus dates from the time when Peel, Yates & Co first introduced cotton-spinning to the town.

CANNOCK

Mill (SJ 988099). Reuben Noden used the waterwheel daily to grind and mix meal for his own farm. The iron wheel, by Bate of Compton and dating from only about 1902, is overshot, 19ft 2in × 5ft 4in, with ten arms. Three of the four pairs of stones are in position, and there is a collection of dressing-tools. An elaborately jointed lever controls the rack and pinion of the pentrough.

CHEADLE

Tollhouse (SK 002430). George E. Hamilton, 'civil engineer' of Walton near Stone, produced drawings and specifications for a toll-house at the west end of Cheadle on the Blythe Marsh–Calton Moor road. Thomas Bull of Oakamoor agreed in September 1832 to build it for £81, the work to be completed by 1 January 1833. Although the bay window is now curved rather than square, and there are no longer leaded lights, the tollhouse is largely in its original condition. George

Hamilton was at pains to make the front elevation symmetrical, so the functional outside door was balanced by a 'blank door' complete with step of Wetley Rock stone.

Railway (SK 008443–035453). At Woodhead was a colliery powered by a 45hp steam engine, and coals from here were taken along the 2 mile tramway to the wharf on the Uttoxeter Canal between Oakamoor and Froghall (035453). In the opposite direction went lime for transfer to the Cheadle road at Woodhead Wharf. A double-track inclined plane, 900ft long, ran through Gibridding Wood. Parts of the railway may be traced on the ground, and stone sleeper-blocks, some of them with the securing spikes in them, can be seen in the wall fronting the field on the Cheadle–Froghall road at Woodhead (010442).

CHEDDLETON

Flint mill (SJ 972526). The two low-breast wheels of Cheddleton flint mill, placed abreast, both with wooden arms, starts and buckets, are a spectacular sight from the main road through the village. The southern wheel, 20ft 5in diameter, has nine arms and 5ft 5in wide buckets; the northern wheel, 22ft diameter, has ten arms and 5ft 9in buckets. In both, a massive pit-wheel and wallower convey the drive to a single pan for grinding flint.

The northern mill of about 1760, is red brick with stone quoins, the ground floor having a vaulted brick roof. A pair of bevels above the grinding pan take the drive to a slack-chain type of hoist and a pump. A lean-to extension on the north contained two settling arks. The southern mill began as a corn mill and was adapted for flint grinding. It is brick on a stone base and similar to the other, except that a crank on the countershaft operated the pump, and the hoist is driven by chain off the waterwheel shaft. To its west is a drying-kiln and store; south-west of the complex are calcining kilns connected to the northern mill by a railway of 1ft 6in gauge.

The mill continued in use until 1963. It has now been restored and is maintained by the Cheddleton Flint Mill Industrial Heritage

Trust. Exhibits so far assembled include a single-stamp mill, edge-runner mills and a Robey 100hp drop-valve reciprocating steam engine—the last to be installed to drive a pottery mill.

Silk factory (SJ 972525). On the left side, parallel to the Caldon Canal, stands a building 97ft × 30ft. The ground floor, cut into the rising ground, is of stone and was originally entered beneath a pediment on the south side. On conversion to a silk factory, two brick storeys fourteen bays long, and a brick stack were added. By 1838 the factory contained 180 dozen spindles for throwing silk and 7 nearly new looms, all worked by a 6hp steam engine. By 1855 the factory was unoccupied.

CHORLTON

Mill (SJ 814391). The sophisticated design, materials and workmanship of Chorlton watermill, proclaim the influence of an architect and of a wealthy landowner, the Duke of Sutherland. The architect's drawings are at the County Record Office. Of stone, and three storeys high, the most distinctive features are the virtually square plan and the mansard roof laid with shaped slates. The keystone over the first-floor door is inscribed 'REBUILT 1848'. The wheel-house and mill-house from the previous mill were retained.

COBRIDGE, see STOKE-ON-TRENT.

COLWICH

Canal junction (SJ 994229). In 1771 the Trent & Mersey Canal was extended from Shugborough to Stone; the following year all the Staffordshire & Worcestershire Canal was open. Their junction is here at Haywood, where the last bridge across the Staffordshire & Worcestershire, No 109, carries the towpath of the Trent & Mersey. The bridge is of red brick and, to allow the turning of boats, of exceptional span.

The toll-keeper's cottage has disappeared. A former stable remains north of Haywood Bridge and, west of the dock, a warehouse is now a

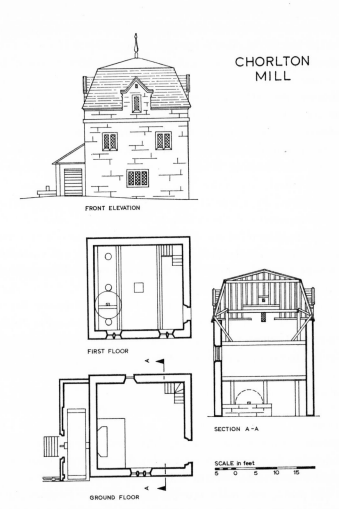

CHORLTON
MILL

FRONT ELEVATION

FIRST FLOOR

SECTION A-A

GROUND FLOOR

SCALE in feet
5 0 5 10 15

Chorlton watermill. Based on drawing (c 1848) at Staffordshire Record
Office, D593/H/12/2/33c

private dwelling. A tollhouse with a hole for the issue of tickets and arched windows with interlaced glazing-bars stands on the south side of the Staffordshire & Worcestershire Canal before it crosses first a mill-stream and then the Trent, by stone aqueducts of one and four arches respectively.

Railway bridge (SJ 997211). In an agreement with the Earl of Lichfield, the Trent Valley Railway was to cross the Lichfield Drive to Shugborough by 'a neat and handsome stone Archway'. The nearness of such reproduction Athenian antiquities as the Tower of the Winds and the Arch of Hadrian encouraged a classical style with balustrades, mask keystones and pairs of Ionic columns. Three plinths rise above the cornice; the outside ones carry a seahorse and a lion—the supporters of the Anson arms—and the taller centre one has the shield-of-arms of the Earl of Lichfield (Anson with quarterings, impaling Philips) backed by the robe of estate and surmounted by a coronet. Circular panels with the Anson crest adorn the outside plinths.

Railway tunnel (SJ 981216–988215). In contrast to the Lichfield Drive bridge, the west portal of Shugborough Tunnel is Norman. The Earl of Lichfield required that it should be 'properly and sufficiently guarded . . . by a Screen or Fence of Close paling to hide the sight of the Trains as they pass in and out'. Structural considerations too favoured a semi-circular arch, and appropriately this rests upon clustered jambs with Norman cushion capitals. The head of the arch is dated '1847' and above is an embattlement and corbel-table with corbels in the form of whirls of foliage and grotesque heads. The impression of a castle gateway is completed by a pair of embattled and buttressed towers and a curtain wall.

The east portal with its cavetto cornice and battered sides suggests the entrance to an Egyptian temple. The quoins of the semi-circular arch have fielded panels alternating with vermiculation. Above is the shield-of-arms of the 1st Earl of Lichfield.

The tunnel itself, 777yd long, 'is driven through a conglomerated gravel of small stones fixed in a matrix of red marl'. Gunpowder had to be used, leading to a fatal accident on 10 January 1846. Junction of the borings was on 31 October 1846.

CONSALL

Plateway (SJ 938446–998492). Consall Plateway, of uncertain date, is shown on the first edition of the Ordnance Survey Map to run from Consall to north of Caverswall. But evidence on the ground shows that it extended beyond Weston Coyney, giving it a total length of more than 6 miles. In 1841, when lime burnt in the six kilns at Consall was being carried to a wharf at Rangemoor on the Potteries–Cheadle turnpike, it was vainly hoped that coals mined at Consall would provide further freight. Some stone sleepers remain, and a stone-faced tunnel under the Leek–Cheadle road (967485), giving its name to Tunnel Farm.

COPPENHALL

Windmill (SJ 898191). The four-storey, brick Butterhill Mill, 28ft diameter at the base, stands on an earth mound, and originally had pairs of entrances, one above the other, north and south. The upper ones served the first floor and were used for loading of waggons. This floor was heated by fireplaces, west and east, and at the oblique points regularly spaced windows light the three upper floors. Three floor beams are in position, and at the top the wooden curb with the iron-geared rack for the fantail drive facing inwards. Enough remains of the cap itself to give an idea of the general design. The cap circle carries the rollers, and the joist between the pairs of sheers helped to support the fan stage.

DRAYCOTT-IN-THE-MOORS

Pumping station (SJ 973395). Cresswell, opened in 1932, must have one of the last pumping steam-engines to be installed—a pair of triple-expansion vertical steam-engines, signed by Hathorn Davey & Co Ltd, Leeds. It is of 4ft stroke; the cylinder diameters are: HP 17in, IP 25in and LP 44in.

K

DUDLEY

Brewery (SO 922862). A small brewery supplying a few public houses, and structurally part of one of them, is now rare. A good example, however, is the Delph, Brierley Hill, where the façade of the Vine Inn is boldly painted with a Shakespearean quotation, besides an advertisement for 'Batham's Traditional Home Brewed Mild & Bitter Beers'. Left of the public house are the hop and malt stores. Behind, the buildings are arranged for gravitational flow.

The firm was founded by Daniel Batham in 1877, and the present Delph Brewery was built in 1905.

Dial Glassworks (SO 893858). The original works was probably founded in 1704 by Joshua Henzey, the younger. The move to the present site at Audnam alongside the Stourbridge Canal presumably took place about 1788, the date that appears on a stone above the entrance of the glass-cone.

A number of the early buildings survive clustered around this glass-cone which, truncated in 1936, was in use with an oil-fired furnace until 1966.

Stuart & Sons Ltd glassworks (SO 894864). In 1961 there were nine surviving glass-cones: two were around Stourbridge, two in the north of England, one in Scotland and the remainder in Germany. In 1966 the cone of Webb Corbett Ltd was truncated, so the Red House glass-cone is now the only one intact for a distance of some 70 miles and is an industrial monument of international importance.

The Red House Works of Stuart & Sons Ltd stands on a ridge to the east of High Street, Wordsley. Its date is uncertain, but probably later than the Stourbridge Canal of 1779 which passes significantly near. Richard Bradley, glass manufacturer, bought the site in 1788 presumably intending either to build a works or develop one.

The cone was essential to most glassworks. Here the glass was melted and worked into its basic shape. The Red House cone is brick, 87ft high, tapering with fair regularity from a diameter of 57ft to one of 10ft. Internally the bottom thickness of the wall is continued above in the form of twelve buttresses. The floor area is now cleared and used for storage, so that the twelve-pot furnace that occupied the centre has disappeared. Subsidiary buildings projected round the cone externally. Anti-clockwise from the entrance on the south side, these were (1) the 'dog-hole' for storage of the pots (2) the pot-arch where the fireclay pots were heated before transference to the main furnace (3) an annealing kiln (4) a metal-room for the storage of the mix ready for melting into glass (5) a glory-hole or small furnace for reheating a vessel during working (6) a second glory-hole and a second kiln and (7) the lehr or tunnel through which the worked vessels passed for controlled cooling. Between (5) and (6) was an entrance for the coal to fire the kilns and glory-holes. The main coal entrance is now blocked; it ran at water level from the canal to the 'cave' or basement of the cone. Apart from the lehr and an associated kiln, these buildings have been removed, but marks in the brickwork remain. The cone continued in use until 1939.

The White House Works, date unknown and on the opposite side of the road, enjoys the same benefit from a canal frontage. In 1883 it was stated as established in 1812, and is on a map of 1824. The cone, 66ft diameter at the base, was truncated in 1939, its nine-pot furnace having remained in use until 1935. Both furnaces were always coal-fired, and the underground passages along which the coal was barrowed and then lifted into the furnace by means of a Frisbie Feed, comprising bucket, chain and winding-gear, are still partly open.

Canal tunnel (SO 932892–947917). The longest canal tunnel in Staffordshire and the fifth longest in England, the Dudley Tunnel connects the Birmingham Canal to the Stourbridge Canal, which latter connects with the Staffordshire & Worcestershire. It avoided the heavy tolls on coal imposed by the Staffordshire & Worcestershire Company. The Act was passed in July 1785, by which date the Dudley Canal Company had completed a canal as far east as Park Head, and Lord Dudley, acting on his own, had constructed a branch to ease the removal of coal and limestone. This branch ran from the Birmingham Canal and ended in tunnel at Castle Mill. What was now needed was a tunnel 3,172yd long, of which 2,942yd would have to be specially built; 34yd would be a basin open to the surface at Castle Mill, and 196yd the tunnel already built by Lord Dudley.

Due to unsatisfactory contractors, the tunnel was not completed until 1792, over four years behind schedule. Even then, a main source of limestone was still inaccessible by canal, but by 1837 Lord Dudley had privately built an extension, 1,227yd long, from Castle Mill basin to an underground basin at Wren's Nest. The tunnel thus assumed its present Y-shaped plan, the three arms radiating from Castle Mill.

ECCLESHALL

Glass furnace (SJ 759312). In Bishop's Wood, a mound, about 6ft high × 11ft diameter, was excavated by T. Pape in 1931, exposing the nearly complete lower part of a rectangular glass furnace. Of large squared sandstone blocks, it was centred on a flue, 20in wide, with a stoke-hole at each end. The interior had sloping sides with base 4ft 5in × 2ft 10in. On either side of the flue was a siege platform, 1ft high, on which to stand the crucibles of molten glass; in fact the bases of four crucibles and of a small pot were found in position. Associated glass included window and vessel fragments.

Now enclosed by a protective hut, it is basically as T. Pape found it, and conveys a good impression of an early glassworks where the flames from the two wood-burning fires would have met under a roof built over the sieges and the flue.

Mill (SJ 791297). Picturesque from across the pond, Walk Mill is now a corn mill but formerly, as its name indicates, was fulling cloth. The high-breast wheel, still used occasionally to work the sack-hoist, is cast-iron with eight arms, and is 18ft × 5ft 4in.

The stone wheel-house is the earliest part of the mill, whose main part, of brick, is likely to date from 1792. When advertised for sale in October 1795, it was stated that a 21 year lease would have 17 years to run at the following Michaelmas, and it may be assumed the signing of the lease coincided with the completion of the rebuilding.

Pumping station (SJ 830339). Dating from 1914, Mill Meece pumping station was designed by William Campbell, architect, of Hanley. Faced externally with red brick, a masonry effect is produced by one-course channels in the pilasters of the engine house. Both engine house and boiler house have semicircular-headed windows; the hipped roofs are covered with handmade tiles and crowned with ventilators. The stack is 125ft high. Inside are two horizontal tandem steam-engines:

Left-hand engine
   1914. By Ashton Frost & Co Ltd, Blackburn
   High-pressure cylinder: 26in diam
   Low-pressure cylinder: 49in diam
   Stroke: 5ft
Right-hand engine
   1927. By Hathorn Davey & Co Ltd, Leeds
   High-pressure cylinder: 27in diam
   Low-pressure cylinder: 52in diam
   Stroke: 5ft

ENDON
   Canal junction (SJ 947537). In 1797 an Act was passed for a reservoir at Rudyard and a cut from there to be primarily a feeder for the summit level of the Caldon Canal but also the main part of a branch canal to Leek town. This branch was opened in 1802. The original summit level had to be extended eastwards to be joined by the new canal, so the canal was re-routed and a staircase of three locks at Hazelhurst substituted for the three widely spaced locks at Endon. The Leek branch left the main canal immediately above the staircase on the north side. Finally, about 1841, perhaps because the staircase was creating congestion or wasting water, the three 'New Hazelhurst Locks' were built and the main canal was diverted northwards to part of its original course. But it was now north of the branch; therefore an aqueduct was built, allowing the main canal to pass under the

branch, where the latter was already carried on embankment over the Endon Brook.

Existing features reflect the various changes. Immediately west of Hazelhurst Junction a turnover bridge takes the branch towpath over the main canal. The iron arch between stone abutments resembles those supplied by the Horseley Ironworks for the Coventry Canal. The parapets, with openwork tiers of semicircles, are cast in one with the ribs, the whole being held at the centre by two plates inscribed '1842'. Beyond stands a large rendered lock-keeper's cottage, its bay window commanding the canal. Eastwards, 700yd, the aqueduct taking the branch over the main canal (954536) is a great whitewashed brick and stone structure, a panel on each side being inscribed 'HAZELHURST AQUEDUCT 1841'. The semicircular arch, corbelled cornice and sloping wing-walls evoke railway architecture; not surprising as the aqueduct was built four years after Staffordshire's first trunk railway was opened.

ENVILLE

Mill (SO 822886). Unused since about 1935, the two-storey brick Mere Mill is exceptional in the extent to which wood rather than iron is used. The overshot waterwheel, 11ft × 3ft 8in, has eight iron arms, but the shaft, sole-boards, shrouds and buckets are wooden, as are the upright shaft, crown-wheel and the countershaft that takes the drive to the sack-hoist.

Windmill (SO 845876). Spittlebrook Mill, 25ft diameter at the base, is in similar condition to Butterhill Mill (p 161) except that the upright shaft is propped up inside. The mill existed by 1820.

ESSINGTON

Windmill (SJ 943036). Essington Mill presents the Midlands type of post-mill where the body is supported by a post but some of the weight is taken by rollers running on a curb. All that remains is the brick roundhouse, 6ft high × 11ft 3in diameter internally, the octagonal post, 2ft 4in across, the crown-tree socketed to the top, and the pair of sheers. On top of the roundhouse is the curb and four of the six rollers.

FARLEY

Wire mill (SK 071426). Thomas Patten & Co, brass manufacturers, began operations at Alton about 1734. By the nineteenth century, the brass was cast into plates at Cheadle, rolled and slitted at Oakamoor and drawn to the required thickness for wire and pins at Alton. On 17 September 1828, the firm decided to remove the wire-mills to Oakamoor to concentrate production there. In 1830 Alton Mill was offered on lease, having three waterwheels. It subsequently became a paper mill, and the three wheels were not scrapped until World War II. The present stone and tiled complex, of various dates, incorporates a petrol-filling station. At the rear, a rectangular block has a stone on the inside south wall inscribed 'TP & CO 1736'.

Railway station (SK 070426). At Alton, Staffordshire's only surviving example of an Italianate railway station dates from about 1849 and is largely in its original state. There are two elements: the single-storey station itself and the three-storey tower where the Earl of Shrewsbury waited in his own suite of rooms.

The station, now Landmark Trust property, matches in style the lodge further up the road. It is strange perhaps that a Gothic treatment was not adopted. In this part of the county Pugin's influence is strongest, and this station served Alton Towers, the seat of Pugin's patron, the 16th Earl of Shrewsbury.

FAZELEY

Calico mill (SK 199021). At Bonehill Mill, now builders' workshops, corn was ground by water power until about 1965. The three pairs of stones have gone; only the waterwheel and pit-wheel remain. The iron breast-shot wheel is 12ft diameter and, at 14ft, exceptionally wide. It has six arms at the centre as well as at either end. The feed channel from the mill-pond crosses the overflow by a bridge and, immediately before the pentrough, is carried on cast-iron columns.

The four-storey brick building is presumably late eighteenth century; a south extension, evidently a kiln, is braced by tie-rods, with seventeen plates inscribed 'NICKLIN BIRMINGHAM 1838'.

The mill may have been associated with the Peel family's calico-printing works. At Bonehill, Robert Peel and his partners insured a cotton mill for £500 in 1797 and a printing-shop for £600 in 1798. In 1823 Edmund Peel and his partners appear to have owned at least twenty-four buildings at Bonehill for processes including block-cutting, pencilling, calendering, drying and dyeing.

Cotton mills (SK 2001). About 1790 the Peel family's interests had reached Fazeley where Robert Peel (see p 57) established two 'extensive' cotton mills besides a calico-printing works at Bonehill. One mill still stands at the end of Mill Lane, near the Birmingham & Fazeley Canal. Known since at least 1851 as Old Mill, it is presumably the building that was first insured in 1795; the mill itself for £1,000, millwright's work at £300, 'clockmaker's work' at £2,500 and stock at £1,200—high sums consistent with the scale of the existing building. The main block, with iron-framed windows, is a brick three-storey range, 164ft long × 33ft wide. At first, evidently only eight bays long, it was extended westwards and by a central staircase wing and two smaller ones on the south side. Inside, abreast at the centre, are two disused turbines; the one partly dismantled was by Frederic Nell of London.

Old Mill belongs to William Tolson Ltd, smallware manufacturers, whose association with Fazeley dates to 1854. Their main production is now concentrated in the 'Steam Mill' (203018), erected in 1883 alongside the Birmingham & Fazeley Canal—an impressive five-storey building, twenty-nine bays long, with corner buttresses.

Fazeley retains some workers' houses including some of three storeys in Coleshill Street. In Mill Lane, a two-storey range of about 1800 showed the influence of mill construction, for brick vaults ran from front to back carrying the first floor and a brick vault carried the roof. Thus, to protect against fire, timberwork was eliminated. The last of these houses were demolished in 1972.

FORTON

Monument (SJ 759217). Its origin as a windmill might be questioned except for the name of the field 'Windmill Piece'. Forton Monument now consists of a tapering stone tower, merging into a conical roof. In 1838 it was surmounted by a ball finial. The conversion from windmill to folly is said to have taken place in 1780—an instance of industry meeting the needs of landscape architecture.

GNOSALL

Mill (SJ 780192). Here, a three-sided block at the north end of a large complex of red brick and tiled buildings is dated 1850. Coley Mill, dated 1842 and disused since 1939, is at the west end of the two-storey central range. It contains conventional corn-grinding machinery and an iron undershot wheel, 16ft 6in × 4ft 3in, with two sets of eight arms. The shafting from the crown-wheel continues into a malthouse that runs at right angles from the mill and has a dismantled kiln at the south end.

HORTON

Mill (SJ 951574). At Harracles Mill, removal of the wheel-house has exposed a fine 16ft × 4ft h gh-breast wheel with eight wooden arms and wooden sole-boards and buckets. The stone-built mill forms a continuation of the mill-house and, although no longer in use, the machinery is among the best preserved in Staffordshire. The gearing is unusual: in particular the crown-wheel is beneath the spur-wheel and both are on the first floor. The coupling device carried on the countershaft projects beyond the waterwheel so as to drive a portable machine such as a saw-bench. The position of the spur-wheel means the stones are over-driven, ie the nuts or pinions engaging the spur-wheel are above the stones instead of beneath. There are four pairs of stones, three of which are driven direct off the spur-wheel and the fourth by two lines of countershaft off the extended teeth of the spur-wheel.

IPSTONES

Flint mill (SK 004484). Consall flint mill was erected by John Leigh, lord of the manor in the 1830s, and by 1845 had assumed its present basic plan. In 1841, when this mill and another, 400yd downstream, were offered for sale, 2 of the 3 iron waterwheels were 'lately new', 30ft diameter, and there were 17 or 18 grinding-pans. In 1848 the output of both mills amounted to 350 tubs of slop per week.

The water supply at Consall Mill comes from the Caldon Canal which at Consallforge, ½ mile upstream, receives the main flow of the River Churnet, the canal thus substituting for the original stream supply. A water-turbine now drives three grinding cylinders, and the only part of a waterwheel remaining is the 19ft 2in long shaft at the west end of the canalside frontage.

The three cylinders where Australian sand and pebbles are ground into glaze for the pottery industry are at the west end of the main building; they discharge direct into a single drying-kiln beneath. Water to mix with the sand and pebbles is stored in a haystack boiler in the roof-space in the centre of the building and is one of the most remarkable features of a remarkable site. Flint is no longer ground at Consall, but a range of eight storage arks line the canal. The complex is completed by a pair of drying-kilns, six calcining kilns and what in 1845 was blacksmith's shop, cottage, office and workshop.

Tollhouse (SK 024502). In 1837 the clerks and surveyor submitted to the trustees a report on the Cheadle turnpike roads, recommending the sale of the existing tollhouse at Ipstones and the erection of a house, gate and bar in place of an existing chain, in a more convenient position. Thus, there is now a tollhouse at the top end of the village, where the road to Butterton Moor End joins that to Foxt.

The house conforms to a design used more than once by the Cheadle trustees. Of brick with a slate roof, it has windows with interlaced Gothic glazing-bars, and a porch projecting from an octagonal extension.

KIDSGROVE

Canal tunnels (SJ 837541–849517). Harecastle Hill, part of the watershed between the Trent and Mersey, presented the greatest single engineering challenge of James Brindley's plan to link four main waterways of England. It could only have been avoided by an inconvenient series of locks and a shorter summit-level; and opportunities to win coal during construction, use the drainage water and take branches direct into the coal seams would have been lost. So Harecastle Tunnel, the first transport tunnel in England and in its day the longest, was started on 27 July 1766.

Fifteen vertical shafts were sunk; two headings from each and one heading at each end meant thirty-two headings could be driven simultaneously. At least one steam engine later supplemented horse power for pumping and haulage. Even so the hard millstone grit, fire-damp from the coal seams and running water all created problems. Not until May 1777 was this last part of the Trent & Mersey Canal open.

The completed tunnel was 2,88oyd long without a towpath. It took about two hours to 'leg' a boat through and, as the 9ft wide waterway only took single-line traffic, congestion soon developed. There was also deterioration of the tunnel as bricks worked loose and debris from its various branches into the coal seams got into the main canal. In 1822 Telford was asked to design a second parallel tunnel; the contract was awarded to Pritchard & Hoof of King's Norton. Fifteen vertical shafts were again sunk, but now cross-headings were driven into the earlier canal, some 25yd west; railways were laid and pumping-engines erected. Work began in summer 1824 and was completed in April 1827. The new tunnel was 46yd longer and 14ft diameter—wide enough to accommodate a towpath.

Telford's tunnel is still in use, but Brindley's is derelict. At Kidsgrove, the entrances still preserve their original appearance. Brindley's entrance on the right has a simple semicircular arch in the brick revetment; Telford's is more imposing with rusticated masonry and stone cornice and coping. At the Stoke end, a rusticated stone retaining wall separates the two, and a pair of staircases giving access to the two-storey tunnel-keeper's cottage completes a symmetrical arrangement. Telford's entrance was concealed in the mid-1950s by a building housing three electric fans for ventilating the tunnel.

Lock and aqueducts (SJ 8354). The Macclesfield Canal was completed in 1831; surveyed by Thomas Telford, the engineering by William Crosley. The first 1½ miles to Hall Green Lock was constructed under an Act of 1827 by the Trent & Mersey Canal Company, and the Staffordshire part of this Hall Green branch includes one notable bridge and two aqueducts. All three are similar, being mainly of blue brick, with stone for such details as the coping, cornice, and the quoins and soffit of the arch. All have rectangular tablets boldly inscribed with Roman lettering. The bridge taking the Trent & Mersey towpath over the branch canal (835545) is inscribed 'MACCLESFIELD CANAL MDCCCXXVIIII'; the aqueduct over the Trent & Mersey Canal (830549) 'POOL LOCK AQUEDUCT MDCCCXXVIIII'. It is immediately preceded by a turnover bridge for the towpath and is followed by a second aqueduct (830550) inscribed 'RED BULL AQUEDUCT MDCCCXXVIII', that takes the Macclesfield Canal over the Tunstall–Liverpool road.

Railway tunnel (SJ 840535–847520). Harecastle Tunnel, 1,768yd long, is by far the longest in Staffordshire. It mostly runs between the two canal tunnels (pp 171–2) but slightly higher, the floor of the rails being 18ft above the water level. It is approached from the north by a second tunnel, 183yd long, and before this by a cutting which, because it passes near Kidsgrove church, was brick-roofed for about 150yd 'so as to secure the worshippers within the sacred edifice from annoyance by the passage of trains'. This roof was replaced by flying buttresses when the line was electrified.

Construction of the main tunnel employed about 1,600 men and 100 horses; 15 intermediate shafts, averaging 140ft deep, had to be sunk. Steam engines raised soil and lowered materials to the workmen, and a horse tramway ran across the top of the hill. A caravan site marks where cottages especially built formed the nucleus of the settlement called Line Houses. George Parker Bidder was engineer, Brassey & Co contractors. The work took under two years, the line opening on 9 October 1848.

Electrification has led to construction of a diversion westwards to avoid the two tunnels. The reason why the present line was not adopted in the first place lies primarily in the resistance of Mr Thomas Kinnersley, owner of Clough Hall. It was also felt that a line with a tunnel would be more direct, gradients would be less and that shafts sunk in construction of the canal tunnels could be re-used (House of Lords RO, Minutes of Evidence, HC, 1846, vol 47, N Staffs Rly, 27 April, pp 24–6, cited by courtesy of Clerk of the Records).

KINGSLEY

Mill (SK 025471). The original two-storey brick and stone Frog-hall Mill may have been built in 1816 when the lease changed hands, since a stone addition is entered through an archway dated '1825' on the keystone. In 1833 the mill ground corn, but now grinds manganese oxide and Australian rutile for colouring bricks and tiles.

There are two undershot waterwheels, both iron apart from wooden starts and buckets. The wheel serving the original block, 15ft 11in × 10ft 9in has three sets of eight arms and drives off the pit-wheel three 10ft grinding pans, two on one countershaft and one on another. The second wheel, disused, served the three-gable brick extension abutting on the south. It is 14ft 11in × 4ft 4in with two sets of eight arms. The headrace for the southern wheel passes over the tailrace of the northern one.

Railway (SK 026476–077486). The name Caldon Canal for the branch canal that joins the Trent & Mersey at Etruria shows that its destination was Caldon rather than Froghall. Nevertheless a rise of 700ft in 4 miles meant the canal had to end at Froghall. From there the journey was completed by only the second railway in the country authorised by Act of Parliament. Four successive lines were built.

The two earliest were in use 1777–1802 and may still be partly traced. The third was constructed under an Act of Parliament of April 1802, with John Rennie as engineer. It too was for horse-drawn traffic but, unlike the first two, incorporated inclined planes and flanged plateway. Its route combined easy gradients with long steep slopes, and the three main inclined planes are readily recognisable as earthworks. The Great Froghall Plane, 303yd long, may be seen from the Ashbourne–Hanley road where it passed over a lane. The abutments of the bridge remain (SK 029475). At the farmhouse at the top of the plane the banksmen operated the endless chain that drew the empty wagons uphill by the weight of the laden ones running down. The other two planes, at Whiston and Cotton, begin in cuttings and end in conspicuous embankments.

In 1849 the North Staffordshire Railway reached Froghall, and the railway company replaced the plateway with a 3ft 6in gauge railway, working on the self-acting principle by cables in four sections.

KINGSTONE

Mill (SK 046287). Blythebridge Mill is one of the few in Staffordshire with architectural pretensions. The whole is of brick and tile; on the visible south elevation the arched openings have square or arched hood-moulds, and the windows have Gothic glazing-bars. Above the central first-floor door is a quatrefoil panel within a circle matching the openings on either side. This panel contains the shield-of-arms of Robert, 7th Earl Ferrers (Ferrers impaling Mundy) and the date '1823'. The wheel and machinery have been removed.

KINVER

Wire mill (SO 848832). In the nineteenth century, Kinver parish contained several forges for the manufacture of bar, rod and sheet iron. One of these, fed by a pool formed from the River Stour, was at Kinver itself. In 1868 the product of Kinver Mill was iron and steel wire, but this ultimately changed to spades and forks.

The site is now partly occupied by a pumping station opened in

1908; all three waterwheels have been removed. One was in a building now used as a saw-mill, still containing two hearths and a stack.

LEEK

Albion Mills (SJ 983561). As Leek's best example of an early multi-storey silk factory, the original part of Albion Mills is officially listed as a building of special architectural or historic interest. Three storeys high 113ft × 27ft, it relies for effect on chequer brickwork, regular spacing of the windows, off-centre doorway in the main elevation and tiled and hipped roof surmounted by a hexagonal cupola, which retains its bell but lacks compass-points and weather-vane. The lavatories, with ornamental cast-iron railings to each balcony, are a later addition at the rear. In 1839 there were ten looms driven by a steam engine. The boiler-house, that contained a vertical boiler, stands to the west; the engine-house has disappeared.

The one firm of Anthony Ward & Co Ltd, established 1815 and now manufacturers of industrial sewing threads in nylon, terylene, silk and cotton, have always owned Albion Mill; their silk manufactory was rated in 1834 at £45. An archway separates the mill from the houses along the west side of King Street; it was part of the same development. Land Tax Returns give completion date as 1828–9.

Silk-workers' houses, King Street (SJ 985562). Albion Street and especially King Street provide the most extensive group of silk-workers' houses surviving in Leek; furthermore it is a compact group, largely in its original form. By the standards of their time the houses are well-built; ceilings are high; main windows are sashes; blue headers produce a chequer effect in the brickwork; and some of the doorways have semicircular fanlights. Cast-iron railings flank the approach to the passage between Nos 28 and 30, King Street, where there were forty-four houses in 1834, of which forty remain. On the west side of the street, Nos 12–46 are shown by the brickwork to be one construction, the deeds of No 14 indicating that this was between 1823, when the land was bought, and 1829, when Nos 12 and 14 were already occupied. Nos 3 and 6 have rainwater heads dated '1825' and '1827' respectively.

The houses, with one exception, are three storeys high, but in nearly all the top floor was not part of the living accommodation. Here the winding, doubling and weaving of silk took place, and to admit enough light, disproportionately long windows, with sliding ventilation frames, were introduced. Sometimes these windows were in both front and rear walls, sometimes at the rear only. It seems from the church rate-books that, on the east side of the street, one house-tenant in each range occupied the full length of its top floor. In 1851 John Ridout, silk manufacturer, had the top floor of Nos 1–19; James Wardle, retired silk merchant, had that of Nos 27–41. On the west side of the street, Nos 6, 8 and 10 are larger houses and were more highly rated. Entirely living accommodation, they were occupied in 1851 by two silk manufacturers and a silk commercial traveller.

Silk-workers' houses, London Street (SJ 985562). John Wreford established a mill in London Street 1823–4, and development of the street began about then. The most striking buildings that remain are thirteen silk-workers' cottages. The jointing in the brickwork shows that the central group, Nos 35–41, were built first. These, with Nos 43–51 to the right, are two storeys high, but Nos 27–33 are three storeys high with former workshops on the top floor. The houses are a humbler version of those in King Street and Albion Street, but distinctive in the Gothic treatment of their windows.

The thirteen houses are shown on a map of 1838 and are probably the property owned by Samuel Milward in London Street. If so they were occupied by 1834.

Big Mill, Mill Street (SJ 979567). The name tersely acknowledges the quality distinguishing it from its predecessors. Six storeys high, twenty-one bays long and five bays wide, it towers above Mill Street on a site rising steeply in both directions. The stone retaining wall along its frontage is pierced symmetrically by two heavy rusticated archways that lead by steps to the central entrance. The mill is predominantly red brick, with emphasis on the ground floor and staircase, both of which have semicircular-headed openings and rusticated quoins. Surmounted by an arcaded belfry, the staircase, far from being an afterthought, is essential to the composition. So are the pairs of lavatories occupying the angles between the staircase and the main part of the mill. A similar treatment of staircase and lavatories is to be found at Waterloo Mills, Waterloo Street, completed in 1894. Internally, the floors of Big Mill are supported at the centre by cast-iron posts, but the roof has traditional timber queen-post construction. It was built early enough to be on a map of 1862 and was designed by William Sugden of Leek.

Wellington Mills, Strangman Street (SJ 981564). The site of Wellington Mills was occupied by an extensive silk-shade in 1838. Of this only the east wing, running back from the road and substantially rebuilt in 1947, survives. The main part of the present frontage is a multi-storey mill displaying the same architectural treatment as had been used over fifty years before for Cross Heath Mills, Newcastle-under-Lyme (see pp 57–8). A pediment inscribed 'WELLINGTON SILK MILLS 1853' rises above the four projecting centre bays as the dominant feature of a severely plain elevation. Of brick except for a stone base, lintels and sills, the mill is four storeys high and fourteen bays long. Staircase and lavatories are in a discreet projection at the rear. The stone flags of the ground floor are partly exposed, all the windows are iron-framed and the roof is of timber king-post construction.

Of special interest is the evidence of former reliance on steam power. The detached building behind the mill and now a workshop was formerly a beam-engine house. The boiler-house complete with stack is still used as such, but the boiler dates from only 1900 and served a horizontal steam engine of 1901 by T. Shore & Sons of Hanley. The owners, Thomas Whittles Ltd, have presented the horizontal engine to the County Museum, Shugborough.

Mill of Messrs Whittles & Son, Strangman Street, Leek (SJ 982564). Although the present owners are corn millers, the property they

L

occupy was formerly a 'shade' for the twisting of silk. In size it is not noticeably inferior to a multi-storey factory; indeed architecturally there is little distinction. The property was for sale in 1859, when it comprised five twisting-rooms about 79ft long × 24ft wide; since when the only major alteration has been the raising of the roof.

Mill (SJ 977569). As a tablet erected jointly by the county council and the district council proclaims, James Brindley worked at Leek Mill from 1742 to 1765. During this period the mill was evidently rebuilt, and the present two-storey structure is the work of the great canal engineer himself—remarkable evidence of the young James Brindley's ability both as millwright and builder.

The architectural qualities are becoming discernible as restoration by a trust proceeds. Originally the doorway was central, but the southern third of the building, probably once Brindley's workshops, has been removed for road-widening. The arched weir controlling the River Churnet remains, the water being led on to an undershot wheel, 16ft × 5ft 6in, of iron apart from eight wooden arms and wooden buckets. Of the machinery, only the great spur-wheel and upright shaft survive intact since Brindley's time, but no doubt all the essential features of the layout are his. There were already pairs of stones in 1836. As at Harracles Mill, Horton (p 169), the spur-wheel has extended teeth and thus conveyed the drive through a pinion and belt to the sack-hoist. A window-quoin on the first floor is inscribed 'TI 1752JB', the second initials being those of James Brindley.

Railway tunnel (SJ 973565–976561). The tunnels at Leek and Cheddleton (980528–980533) had no masonry at either entrance to give them the appearance of natural caverns in the rock; to heighten the illusion it was proposed when the line was opened in 1849 to cover the rock with plants indigenous to the neighbourhood. Only the north portal of Leek Tunnel retains its original appearance: an arch formed of irregular voussoirs rests on jambs of living rock.

LICHFIELD

Malthouse, Upper St John Street (SK 118091). This malthouse is the only obvious industrial building in W. H. Crompton's isometric view of Lichfield of 1862. A stack and engine house immediately to the west have disappeared, but the malthouse itself, despite conversion to a garage and builder's store, is little altered. The building, 102ft × 63ft, is of blue brick, with red brick for the recessed parts. Windows have cast-iron diagonal grills. At the west end, the upper floor is still partly supported by wooden beams and five rows of six cast-iron columns. At the east end, the northern two-thirds comprises the kiln, dated externally '1858'. The ground floor has a barrel-vaulted passage surrounding the furnace chamber; above is a double queen-post roof and a floor of the usual perforated quarries.

Railway bridge, St John Street (SK 118091). This street is the principal approach to Lichfield from the south-east, and it was appropriate that the bridge providing a crossing for the South

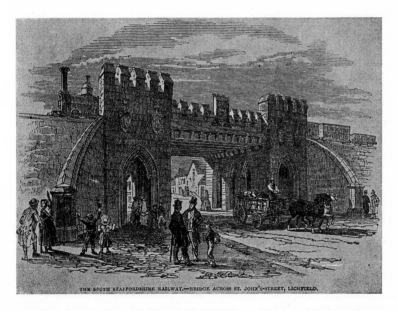

St John Street railway bridge, Lichfield. From *Illustrated London News*
14 April 1849

Staffordshire Railway should evoke a city gateway. Thomas Johnson
of Lichfield was the architect. An engraving shows that the bridge
originally consisted of a horizontal span between two towers, the
whole embattled and pierced with arrow loops. There were sweeps
on each side, and pedestrian-ways passing under Gothic arches
through the towers, and separated by three further arches from the
central carriageway. The main decoration was heraldic, designed and
given by Richard Greene, a Lichfield banker.

In 1849, when the bridge was opened, the side shown in the engraving had the arms of England above the central span and the four
bishops' arms above the entrance to the pedestrian-ways. Subsequent
track widening necessitated drastic reconstruction including transfer
of the shields to their new positions. The pedestrian-ways were demolished in 1969.

Pumping station (SK 112084). Under the South Staffordshire
Waterworks Act, 1853, the company was authorised to supply water
to Lichfield, Walsall, Wednesbury and other Black Country towns.
At first the sole source of supply was Sandfields Pumping Station
opened, as a tablet records, by Lord Ward on 26 October 1858. The
original complex, designed by John Robinson McClean, engineer,
and Edward Adams, architect, comprised a single engine house with
houses for nine boilers to the east. McClean, Adams and the builders,
Branson & Gwyther of Birmingham, were all associated with railways,
hence the influence of railway architecture.

The engine house until 1967 contained two horizontal uniflow
condensing steam-engines, very similar to a gas-engine. Built by
Sulzer Brothers, London, they were installed in 1924 to meet the
situation created by the construction of a comprehensive filtration
plant. Previously, as a tablet records, there had been three James
Watt single-cylinder rotative beam-engines originally intended for
the ill-fated South Devon Atmospheric Railway Company to drive
vacuum pumps. Each engine had a double-acting steam cylinder,
46in diameter, 8ft stroke. The total cost of the works was about
£130,000.

In 1873 a Cornish beam-engine by J. Davies of Tipton was added. Although no longer in use, this survives in an engine house styled like the original buildings, and now the only part of the complex to be retained. It has a 65in cylinder and 9ft stroke. Ram and bucket pumps on the same pump-rod were worked from the beam, and it could pump 2 million gallons per day at 7 strokes per minute. A Tuscan arcade of three arches with fluted keystones supports the bearings for the beam. The whole construction—even the smallest moulding—illustrates the close relationship between architecture and engineering that was still instinctive in the second half of the nineteenth century.

The South Staffordshire Waterworks Company are to be congratulated on the public spirit and foresight that has preserved this, the most monumental of the Staffordshire pumping engines.

LONGNOR

Mill (SK 085646). With those at Cheddleton (p 157) and Froghall, Kingsley (p 173), this is the last working watermill used other than to grind meal. Longnor Mill is the workshop of the Harpur-Crewe Estate, and the 14ft 6in × 5ft 7in pitchback waterwheel is of iron except for the two sets of twenty wooden arms. It is fed by a leat off the River Manifold and has a pit-wheel on either side. Two circular saws, a planer and a morticing-machine are driven off the southern wheel.

LONGTON, see STOKE-ON-TRENT.

MADELEY

Mill (SJ 752460). The three-storey blue-brick building of Wrinehill Mill is now surrounded by modern additions. Electric power replaced water power in 1966, but the large mill-pond, waterwheel, pit-wheel, wallower, spur-wheel, crown-wheel and sack-hoist all remain. The waterwheel is high-breast, 11ft 6in × 5ft, entirely of iron and having six arms.

MAVESYN RIDWARE, see ARMITAGE.

MAYFIELD

Cotton mill (SK 158447). In 1792 the ancient corn and leather mill at Mayfield was said to be in a capital situation for a cotton mill (*Leicester Journal*, 21 September 1792). The conversion was carried out, the owners from 1794 to 1801 being Cooper, Dale and Co.

The oldest building and the only one shown on the tithe map is No 1 Mill. Lying along the mill-stream and still with its turbine, it is fifteen bays long. It began three storeys high, was raised to five storeys but, in 1970, became one storey high. The floor is supported by four rows of four cast-iron columns, cast-iron beams and brick vaults— comparable to Tean Mill (p 61).

The other mills are faced with stone and lack the brick vaulting. No 2 Mill was demolished in 1970. No 3 and No 4 Mills, to the east, run at right angles to the stream and on either side of it, separated by a narrow yard from No 1 and the site of No 2. The mills themselves are undated, but the office block between mills Nos 3 and 4 is dated '1871' and a southern extension to No 4 Mill is dated '1883'.

Housing at Mayfield is equally significant. Above the mills and surrounded by a formal garden lies the brick and stone mill-owner's mansion, now a canteen and works' club. Between the mill-stream and the River Dove are forty-one workers' cottages, arranged in five terraces, the oldest being the two parts of Mayfield Terrace, dated 1856.

MILWICH

Mill (SJ 977314). The small derelict brick building of Coton Mill retains the waterwheel and much of the machinery. Pitchback, 14ft 5in × 5ft 7½in, the wheel is entirely of iron. The two sets of six arms are braced by perforated wedges, similar to those at Wood Mill (p 206), Yoxall. Two pairs of millstones, complete with their tuns, were driven by customary gearing, but the way in which the stone nuts were thrown out of gear by slip-cogs is rare.

In the north-west corner of the mill is a kiln which existed in March 1833, at which time the machinery of the mill was entirely new.

MODDERSHALL VALLEY, see STONE RURAL.

NEWCASTLE-UNDER-LYME

Silk mill (SJ 849466). In 1830 'all that valuable and capacious Silk Mill and Factory, called the Brampton Silk Mill, situated near the town of Newcastle-under-Lyme, and on the banks of the Upper Canal' was for sale, described as having been erected 'only a few years'. It contained a 12hp steam engine by Peel & Williams of Manchester, together with a 14hp boiler.

The mill, 136ft × 34ft externally, is three storeys high with an original staircase at the north-east corner, but the brick walls were mostly rendered and the cast-iron window frames replaced in 1960 when the top storey was removed.

Blast furnace (SJ 821499). The introduction of coke-using blast furnaces into north Staffordshire is indicated by the furnace at Apedale of 1768 and by the former existence at the Apedale iron-works of a triangular tablet of pig-iron inscribed 'APEDALE 1789'. This Springwood furnace presumably belongs to the late eighteenth century, and is the last such structure remaining in the county. The rectangular brick tower is about 40ft high. Each of the four sides had a distinctive function: on the north a former ramp allowed barrows to be wheeled to the top of the furnace; on the south, at ground level, an arch leading to a smaller arch, both in the thickness of the furnace, provided the outlet for extracting the iron; on the west, a similar but smaller system of arches was the outlet for extracting the slag; on the east a flue near the ground admitted the draught that entered the furnace through a series of holes.

A steam engine was needed to operate the bellows. Possibly, before becoming a school, the large brick building to the south of the furnace was the engine house, but its relationship to the furnace does not seem to justify this theory. Other buildings nearby include a planned group of five brick cottages dating from the mid-1800s.

Chimney stack (SJ 816488). Watermills Colliery operated until about 1900, but all that remains is the base of the chimney stack—an impressive object, set on the edge of woodland. The red-brick tower has a stone coping and a receded panel on each of the four sides decorated with intersecting chevrons in white brick. Above are stone panels, inscribed as follows 'R.E.H. A.D. 1840', 'BE JUST & FEAR NOT' 'LIVE & LET LIVE' and 'REGARD THE END'. The initials stand for Richard Edensor Heathcote, the colliery owner.

NORBURY

Mill (SJ 751240). Although disused since about 1900 and now derelict, Weston Jones Mill well illustrates a typical layout. The pond is dry, but an impressive stone revetment still contains a pair of flood gates. The iron breast-shot wheel, 14ft 3in × 4ft, is attributed on stylistic evidence to Massey of Newport. A virtually intact wire-machine for flour dressing, in the corner on the first floor, was driven by a pulley on the countershaft from the crown-wheel. On the top floor are copious bins and a hoist driven off the waterwheel shaft.

Canal junction (SJ 793228). The Newport branch of the Birmingham & Liverpool Junction Canal, opened 1833, leaves the main canal at Norbury Junction and, by joining the Shrewsbury Canal at Wappenshall, provided a route for the carriage of Coalbrookdale iron. The branch was abandoned in 1944 but, during its heyday, Norbury Junction had all the facilities of a great entrepot.

This greatness is partially evidenced by surviving buildings. In a clockwise circuit round the main basin, the first building to the north is the modernised Junction Inn. Opposite, a warehouse converted to a shop and office is followed by the British Waterways Board maintenance yard for the lengths of canal from Audlem Lock to Autherley and from Autherley to Gailey. In the large blue-brick workshop in the centre a vertical steam-engine drove two saws, a steam-box, a drill, a grindstone and a mortar-mill. The works' bell hangs at the north end of the roof while, inside, the boarded floor marks the extent of a former dry dock, approached from the basin. Behind are stores and a smithy. The circuit ends with a lock-keeper's cottage and with a basin and dry dock that was formerly the first lock on the Newport branch.

PENKRIDGE

Railway viaduct (SJ 920144). Penkridge Viaduct is the most notable work on the Staffordshire part of the Grand Junction Railway opened 1837. Thomas Brassey, the contractor who built it for £6,000, regarded it as his earliest important undertaking. Each of the seven arches has a 30ft span and is 37ft high.

QUARNFORD

Spinning mill (SJ 993660). A ¼ mile gated road leads to what must have been one of the least accessible of Staffordshire sites, yet such was the prosperity of the textile industry, inviting exploitation of water power, that a considerable spinning mill flourished at Gradbach.

The existing stone buildings can be compared with a newspaper description of 1837. The dwelling-house is still 'three stories high, cellared, with dining and sitting rooms to the front: store room and counting-house adjoining'. The mill that contained 1,784 spindles for spinning tow and flax, 25yd × 12yd, is ten bays long, with stacks at each end, wooden-framed windows, king-post trusses and stone-tiled roof. A lean-to projection to the east contains the staircase. The waterwheel which occupied the separate building at the south end has gone, as has all machinery.

ROCESTER

Cotton mill (SK 113392). Rocester Mill—later Tutbury Mill—was a corn and fulling mill when Richard Arkwright bought it for £820 in October 1781. The following May, Arkwright had much enlarged it, and in 1783 a water cornmill and cotton manufactory occupied the site. The part dating from 1781–2 is the north-south range, 186ft × 30ft, at the eastern limit of the complex, 24 bays long, 2 bays wide, and 4 storeys high. The walls above foundation level are mainly red brick, ornamented by the lintels of the windows and projecting quoins of the southernmost bay. Inside, the intermediate floors and roof are supported by oak beams, subsequently reinforced by cast-iron columns. As evidenced by the surviving bricked-up arches, power was by two wheels.

The first extension runs westwards at right angles from the centre of the original building. Similar in design and construction, it is four storeys high and twelve bays long; a projecting staircase on the south side and arches at the east end mark the site of two former waterwheels.

In 1831 the mill was for sale or lease with two of the three waterwheels made by Hewes of Manchester and a force of 70hp derived from the River Dove. The property, which included 'an excellent Dwelling-House and thirty-nine Cottages', presented 'to capitalists not only a safe and beneficial investment for the purposes of business, but a respectable, retired, healthy and comfortable country residence'.

The 'Dwelling-House' is Millholme, the brick and stone mansion on the opposite side of the road. Of the 'thirty-nine Cottages', a two- and three-storey red-brick terrace of twenty survives along the north side of High Street.

By 1833 there was a second extension, four storeys high, southwards at right angles to the first one. A central four-storey block was added soon after 1876 when the two brothers, Walter John Lyon and Charles William Lyon, transferred their business from Tutbury (p 58) and renamed the property. The two water-turbines, *Oxford* and *Cambridge*, that replaced the waterwheels about 1876 were in use until 1943. The building containing the beam-engine, probably installed about 1833, survives as a pump-house.

RUGELEY

Pumping station (SK 038194). Brindley Bank station has the date '1905' inscribed over the doorway and by then Gothic severity had given way to a homely sixteenth-century style.

Inside, a steam engine is kept in immaculate condition; it operated until October 1968. Designed to pump 1·25 million gal per day at 18rpm and made by Hathorn Davey & Co, Leeds, it is 90ft 6in long and of horizontal tandem compound construction. Stroke is 5ft; the HP and LP cylinders are 28in and 54in diameter respectively; the fly-wheel weighs 24 tons and is 24ft diameter. The simple D-slide valves seem incongruous in so large an engine.

SANDON

Railway station (SJ 946292). Sandon and Alton (p 167) are the only Staffordshire survivals of railway stations designed primarily to meet the needs of a landed estate. At Sandon the style and details are similar to those at Stone (p 194), but the plan is a T, the stem of which incorporates a porte cochère for the Earl of Harrowby's carriage. The size of the station mainly results from the provision of separate apartments, including a waiting-room, for the earl. Building was in progress when the line opened on 1 May 1849.

SEIGHFORD

Mill (SJ 877277). The three-storey brick Worston Mill with tiled roof and iron window-frames is powered by an undershot wheel, 16ft 3in × 6ft 1½in diameter, with eight arms and entirely of iron, except for wooden starts and floats. It formerly drove four pairs of stones off the spur-wheel and one pair off the countershaft. The date of the building and probably also of the wheel is provided by an oval tablet inscribed 'J. MILNER. 1814'.

SHEEN

Mill (SK 099613). Although the southern half of Brund Mill's three-storey stone and tiled building has collapsed, enough survives to make this the best illustration in Staffordshire of a watermill using stones for grinding, yet fully exploiting new materials and engineering techniques. The 16ft × 6ft 5in high-breast wheel, with two sets of eight wooden arms and wooden sole-boards and buckets, drives, through a system of four gear wheels, a layshaft on which are mounted five bevels, four for the pairs of stones and one for the crown-wheel. In addition a pulley takes the chain for the sack-hoist on the top floor. The machinery of the layshaft is all a single installation, and cast iron is used for the pairs of columns supporting the stones and for the horses above the tuns.

STAFFORD

Mill (SJ 921229). The three-storey brick and tiled Stafford Mill, its stone tablet inscribed 'G.B. 1834', was demolished in 1957. Thanks to the attitude of Stafford Corporation, the two undershot waterwheels with their pit-wheels were retained, and parapet walls added to the stone- and brick-lined pits. Both wheels are entirely of iron with two sets of six arms: the northern one, 12ft diameter across the starts, has buckets 7ft 3in wide; the southern one is 13ft × 11ft 6in. Two of its arms are inscribed on the inside 'G. BREWSTER. 1845'. George Brewster was then the miller.

Windmill (SJ 918232). The largest of the surviving Staffordshire windmills, this derelict tower stands 48ft 6in high from the pavement to the top of the stonework. A re-set circular cast-iron plate is inscribed '1796 I.W.' and it is said to be built with materials from the former Shirehall.

The mill in 1831 was already seven storeys high and contained three pairs of stones, two dressing-mills and a smut-machine. By 1847 steam power, explaining the present brick stack, had been introduced, and the number of stones had risen to five.

Malthouse, Water Lane (SJ 921230). George Brewster was maltster as well as corn miller (above). No sooner had he rebuilt the watermill than he started to erect a malthouse nearby. This, of red brick with iron window-frames and a tiled roof, is 63ft long and about 50ft wide. The symmetrical street elevation carries a stone tablet inscribed 'GB 1837', and there were loading doors to the penultimate bays. The kiln at the south-east corner contains two furnace chambers surrounded by a system of brick-vaulted passages. Three of the cast-iron furnace doors are in position. The upper floors would have been for storage; the only working-floor for turning the malt would have been the basement where the coolness was an asset and where the seven brick vaults are supported by segmental arches springing from stone piers. These piers, three to an arcade, have tapering circular columns and square abaci.

STANTON

Tollhouse (SK 109477). Like that at Ipstones (p 170), Stanton toll-house, now called Y-Bwthyn, represents an attempt to improve the organisation of the Cheadle Turnpike Trust. Rather than rebuild the inconvenient tollhouse at Calton Moor a new house, at the point where the Stanton road branched from the main Blythe Marsh–Calton Moor road, was erected. Although it is dated '1845' on the east gable, its site was not finally conveyed to the trustees until 1847.

STOKE-ON-TRENT

Boundary Works, King Street, Longton (SJ 907437). The sym-metrical frontage is typical of a nineteenth-century Staffordshire pottery. The centre five bays are three storeys high, the roof is hipped and the wide centre bay containing the archway breaks for-ward and is elaborately detailed. Above the flat elliptical archway rises the first-floor venetian window, its three-light division con-tinued in the segmental window of the second floor. The pediment with dentilled cornice carries a tablet inscribed '1819'. Two-storey wings, each of six bays, complete the frontage on each side.

Elder Works, Waterloo Road, Cobridge (SJ 875488). The Steven-sons were making pottery on the present site in 1775; by the early 1830s they were successful enough to employ 600 persons. Under the Stevensons the works reached its present size and assumed its present basic plan but, until after 1878, the site was not entirely industrial. Hawthorn Street to the north had not yet been built. Instead there were gardens and a drive that led to the master potter's house behind the works. The owners from about 1835 to 1910 were the Alcocks, and they built the simple but impressive brick frontage. Channelled pilasters divide the front elevation into ten bays, and a wide one towards the south end has a semicircular-headed archway reaching the full two-storey height of the building. The imposts bear the initials 'J.A.' (John Alcock) and '1848'. The roof is slated and hipped. Internally only traces of the early nineteenth-century pottery survive; in 1968 the last remaining four ovens were demolished.

Etruria Works, Etruria (SJ 869473). The Newcastle to Leek road had just been turnpiked, construction of the Trent & Mersey Canal just begun, when Josiah Wedgwood moved his pottery from its restricted site in Burslem to that point in the Fowlea Brook Valley where the road and the new canal would cross. The works, completed 1769, was the nucleus of an industrial village that he named Etruria; it eventually included workers' cottages and a mansion for Wedgwood himself. The initial size of the works and the concept of a self-contained industrial community were revolutionary—a visible expression of their originator's foresight and business acumen.

In 1968 the works' site was levelled, but one can still see how, due to subsidence, it eventually lay about 12ft below the level of the adjoining canal. The only early building remaining is a circular brick structure that is prominent in a 1794 drawing—26ft diameter, it has two tiers of windows, the four upper ones on the east being circular, and a domed tiled roof. Its purpose is uncertain but it may be circular only because there was a balancing bottle oven at the other end of the façade. Etruria Hall itself, however, still commands the valley from the east. Completed in 1770, it was originally a three-storeyed brick house, and is now the offices of Shelton Iron & Steel Ltd.

Etruscan bone and flint mill, Etruria (SJ 872468). The circuitous approach by road contrasts with accessibility by canal which determined the choice of site. The works is served by a basin off the Trent & Mersey Canal and lies strategically near the junction with the Caldon Canal. The present owners are Jesse Shirley & Son Ltd, who claim to have been established in 1820 and who grind bone for the pottery industry as Stuart Roy & Co Ltd do in the Moddershall

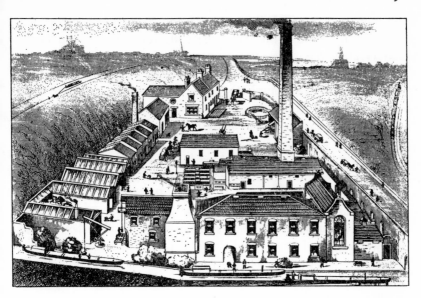

Etruscan Bone Mill, Stoke-on-Trent. From invoice discontinued 1973

Valley (p 195). The chief difference is that until 1972 Etruscan Mill relied on steam rather than water for power. The successive processes are represented by 3 wood-fired kilns, 12 grinding-pans, 3 wash-tubs, 5 underground storage-arks and 3 coal-fired drying-kilns.

The steam engine that drove the pumps and grinding-pans replaced a 10hp condensing engine that was for sale in 1860. The engine house with shaped gables, lying immediately west of the mill containing the grinding-pans, is inscribed 'ETRUSCAN BONE & FLINT MILL ERECTED 1857 J.S.' The engine itself, *Princess*, is of beam construction, said to have been built by Sherratt of Salford and rebuilt by Kirk of Etruria when moved to the present site. It is of 40–46ihp, has a $31\frac{5}{8}$in cylinder and 5ft stroke, and rotated at 24rpm. The boiler pressure was 50lb per square inch, and the water for the boiler was pumped from the Trent & Mersey Canal.

Hill Works, Westport Road, Burslem (SJ 866499). Rebuilt in 1814 by John and Richard Riley who made china, earthenware and Egyptian black, the Hill Works best illustrates the variant of the pottery plan where the entrance was at a corner rather than in the centre of a side. An oval plaque is inscribed 'HILL WORKS 1814'. The lower end was completely rebuilt in the 1960s, and no bottle ovens survive.

Colliery (SJ 884532). The Chatterley Iron Company was registered in 1865, and in 1872 it acquired the leasehold of Whitfield Colliery to obtain suitable coal for its three blast furnaces. Introduction of electrical power has transformed the colliery, and the only steam plant remaining is that serving Hesketh Pit, from which coal was first wound in September 1918. It is a winding-engine with 36in cylinder, 6ft stroke, and Corliss valves made by Worsley Mesnes Ironworks Ltd of Wigan and dated 1914. Two houses for former engines are noteworthy: that of Winstanley Pit is of German design; that of Institute Pit dated '1875' was for a vertical engine, but is now partly demolished.

Railway station (SJ 879456). The headquarters of the North Staffordshire Railway Company, Stoke-on-Trent station was by far the most notable of their buildings, its architectural interest being high enough to be officially recognised. The opening took place on 9 October 1848.

The station largely retains its Jacobean form. The main block, which extended as far as the gabled cross-wings, lies east of the line. Three doors led from the arcade, now enclosed, into the booking-hall, on each side of which were two waiting-rooms. Beyond was a refreshment room on the north side, and a parcels office on the south side. On the first floor, occupying the same width as the booking-hall, is the board room.

Despite conversion to a trains office, the oak panelled walls, panelled ceiling, and above all the proportions, still evoke the grandeur of those early company meetings in this room with its striking bay window projecting over the centre of the arcade. Said to be modelled on a window at Charlton House, Wiltshire, it was claimed in 1848 to be 'in size and magnificence unrivalled perhaps in modern times in this or any other country'. Both arcade and bay window have elaborate friezes and open-work parapets, and the centrepiece of the exterior is a shaped pediment containing the company's arms. The board room was flanked by two committee rooms and two rooms for the secretary and his clerks. The rest of the eastern block had such multifarious uses as audit office, fire-proof room, messengers' rooms and electric telegraph office. The canal offices were in the south cross-wing, and those of the railway in the north cross-wing.

To avoid the danger of crossing the track there were two passenger approaches to Stoke-on-Trent station, but the second booking-office complete with arcade and waiting-rooms to the west of the line is disused.

The station's architect was H. A. Hunt of Parliament Street, London; John Jay of London Wall was the contractor as from 20 July 1847. The sumptuous architecture was criticised by some of the shareholders. Opposite the station, the North Stafford Hotel, opened in June 1849, is part of the same architectural group.

Railway bridge (SJ 909436). There must be few towns where, as at Longton, a railway straddles the centre of the market place. Complications of ownership delayed this part of the line, and the bridge was not complete when the line was opened on 7 August 1848. In its original form, Lane End viaduct, as it was called, consisted of 'seven brick arches, several cast-iron girder bridges, and one wrought-iron bridge of 85 feet span, with bearings constructed on the tubular principle'. The present bridge, a bow-string lattice-girder one designed by G. J. Crosbie-Dawson, was completed on 23 June 1889, at a cost of £4,000. The skew span measures 126ft on the north, and 142ft on the south, side. The intact western abutments bear the shield-of-arms of the North Staffordshire Railway.

STONE

Mill (SJ 905340). Corn is still ground in the four-storey brick
M

Weaver's Mill. An exceptionally large spur-wheel, 13ft 3in across, survives, but a turbine supplemented by electricity replaces the waterwheel. The feed is from a leat, which enters the mill by a bridge at second-floor level. The inscription on the front, 'R.B. Erected in the Year MDCCLXXXXV' is explained by a deed of 1797 which refers to 'the new water Corn mill and buildings lately erected . . . by . . . Robert Bill'. In 1811 an overshot wheel, 24ft diameter, with buckets 5ft 9in wide drove four pairs of stones for grinding flour, and one for shelling oats. In a separate building a second wheel, 22ft × 6ft, worked at night for grinding flint.

Brewery (SJ 901339). Deeds show the site of Stone Brewery has been in the hands of maltsters and brewers continuously since at least 1719. In 1785 Francis Joule came to Stone, and in 1797 he acquired the White Horse Inn which stood on the site of the present brewery offices.

The main approach to Stone Brewery is from the High Street. Left of the carriageway is the former brewer's house, a fine piece of architecture probably erected soon after 1797, followed by the mash-house and malt and hop stores. Above and to the right of the carriage-way are the offices, behind which is the fermenting house, partly dating from 1887. A remarkable feature is the elaborate network of cellars that extends below the malt-stores where the ceiling is supported by early cast-iron columns, and below the brewer's house where two long brick-vaulted corridors continue to the High Street frontage.

Railway station (SJ 896345). Here, at Stone, is a smaller, simpler version of Stoke-on-Trent station (p 192). The finial-topped gables recur, also the mullioned windows and patterned brickwork. The road frontage is three bays wide and two storeys high. Scrolled cartouches decorate the two outside gables, and on the ground floor an open arcade led through a central archway, now blocked, to the booking-hall with its panelled ceiling. At the front, left and right, were the first-class gentlemen's waiting-rooms. At the rear, in the single-storey part, were the two first-class ladies' waiting-rooms, separated by corridors from the gentlemen's. This duplication was necessary because the station occupies an island site with the main Colwich line on the east, and the Norton Bridge branch on the west.

Stone station was designed by H. A. Hunt and built by Brassey & Co, who were also the contractors for the line. Their offer to complete the work for £5,200 was accepted on 11 May 1848.

STONE RURAL

Bone mill (SJ 912350). At Hayes Mill, the waterwheel, described in 1860 and similar to that at Coppice Mill, drove through a pit-wheel and wallower a single pan. The wash-tub to the south was hand-operated until 1968, and discharges the slip into three settling arks. The building east of the wheel contains a drying-kiln, and there is a separate row of four brick cottages.

Like its neighbour, Ivy Mill, Hayes Mill stopped grinding bone in 1965, but the subsequent processing of bone for bone china is still performed here.

Flint and bone mill (SJ 916354). A paper mill in 1844, Ivy Mill was adapted to flint grinding by 1851, and has been altered little since described in 1860. The high-breast waterwheel, 18ft 8in × 6ft 2in, has the same combination of iron and wood as those at Coppice, Hayes, Mostylee and Top mills. A pit-wheel and wallower took the drive to the two pans mounted on the same upright shaft, the upper pan being disconnected by means of a turret clutch.

Water power has not been used since 1965, but bone is still processed in the single wash-tub and pair of settling arks. The calcining of flints was formerly done on the site; two kilns remain beside the semicircular weir away from the main range of buildings.

Flint mill (SJ 920366). Top Mill resembled Cheddleton Mill (p 157) originally in so far as there were two waterwheels side by side. The south wheel went about 1915; the survivor, 15ft 6in × 5ft 7½in wide, is overshot, and its seven arms, sole-boards and floats, are wooden. It drove through a pit-wheel and wallower a single pan, the cast-iron sweeps of which are signed by Jones & Edwards of Longton and therefore are not earlier than about 1895.

Top Mill, of all the mills in the Moddershall Valley, is perhaps the best place to study flint grinding. The flints were first calcined in the double kiln at the east end of the complex then, ground and mixed with water, they passed as slip from the pan to the belt-driven wash-tub, where the slip was agitated. It then settled in one of three arks, before being brought to the desired consistency in the drying-kiln.

STRETTON near BURTON-UPON-TRENT

Sewage pumping station (SK 262258). Sewage disposal has been a problem at Burton-upon-Trent because of the poor fall and the quantities of water discharged from the breweries. It was decided to erect a pumping station at Clay Mills and pump all the sewage 3 miles northwards to a farm at Etwall.

The four steam engines that did the pumping until 1971 are contained in two red brick engine houses and are the largest of their kind in Staffordshire. They date from 1885 and represent beam construction in its latest and most elaborate phase.

Type: Rotative double-acting compound condensing engines, each driving two ram force-pumps
Makers: Gimson & Co, Leicester
Cylinders: HP 24in diameter × 6ft stroke
            LP 38in diameter × 8ft stroke
Fly-wheels: 24ft diameter, each weighing 24 tons
Beams: 28ft long, 4ft deep at centre, each weighing, exclusive of trunnions, 13 tons
Steam pressure: 80lb per square inch
Horse power: 140 (each engine)
Capacity of each engine: 130,000gal per hour to a height of 110ft at a speed of 12rpm

Beside two of the engines, emphasising their size, is a small engine,

4in diameter × 6in stroke, used for turning the main fly-wheels in starting, cleaning and repairing.

STRETTON near STAFFORD

Canal aqueduct (SJ 872107). In the course of its 39½ miles, the Birmingham & Liverpool Junction Canal crosses over two turnpike roads by similarly constructed aqueducts, one being over the Nantwich–Chester road in Cheshire.

At Stretton, where the canal crosses Watling Street (not, however, Telford's Holyhead road) there is a cast-iron trough with sides formed of five flanged plates bolted together; support is provided by six ribs, each comprising a pair of spandrel-shaped castings that abut against the single ridge-piece, which had to be stepped because of the skew construction. The central plate on each side of the trough is inscribed:

BIRMINGHAM AND LIVERPOOL CANAL.

THOS. TELFORD, F.R.S.L. & E.

ENGINEER.

WM. HAZLEDINE, CONTRACTOR.

1832.

Telford was a Fellow of the Royal Societies of London and Edinburgh; Hazledine was the Shrewsbury ironfounder closely associated with him. The line of inscription giving Hazledine's name and status has deliberately been erased—to placate the Wilson brothers who, as contractors for the whole canal from Church Eaton to Autherley, might have felt that either no name or their own should appear?

SWYNNERTON

Tollhouse (SJ 851393). The Newcastle–Eccleshall Turnpike Trust was set up under an Act of 1823, and because Knowl Wall was part of his estate, the plans and specifications for the brick and tiled tollhouse there have survived among the Duke of Sutherland's papers. The centre door gave access to a lobby. On the left, through a door,

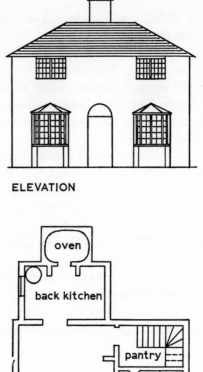

ELEVATION

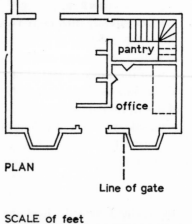

oven

back kitchen

pantry

office

PLAN

Line of gate

SCALE of feet

5   0   5   10   15

Knowl Wall tollhouse, Swynnerton. Based on drawing (1825) at Staffordshire
Record Office, D593/H/12/2/123a

was the living room. On the right was the office, where tickets were issued and money held. Kitchen and oven were a single-storey annexe; the staircase occupied a corner with the pantry. A separate privy was to stand behind. The centre door is now blocked, square bay windows under a continuous lean-to roof replace the canted ones, and extensions have altered the internal plan.

In May 1825, Charles Winks submitted an estimate to build this tollhouse for £172 10s.

Pumping station (SJ 829370). A lavish combination of Hollington stone with buff and brown bricks results in the extraordinary polychromy of Hatton Pumping Station. The most prominent feature is the two-storey block that contained a beam pumping-engine, entered beneath an arch inscribed 'STAFF[RE] POTTERIES WATER WORKS 1890'. Associations with plenty and water are conveyed by a cornucopia and scallop-shell on the keystone and by fish-head corbels to niches on each side. Inside, the ground floor is divided by fluted columns with elaborate acanthus capitals, necessary to take the weight of the engine beam. A brass plaque commemorates the opening of the works in 1893. The engine house has urns at the parapet corners, and the square staircase turret at the north-west ends in an open balcony and pyramidal roof surmounted by a cast-iron finial.

North-west of the beam-engine house is a similar but single-storey block that contained a horizontal tandem engine. Completing the triangle on the north-east is a third block, dated '1898', that contained a simple horizontal engine.

The space between the engine houses is occupied by gabled boiler-houses; workshops lie behind.

TAMWORTH

Railway viaduct (SK 213037). Described in 1851 as contributing to the general beauty of the Tamworth scenery, the viaduct that crosses the Anker Valley was the most expensive engineering work of the Birmingham & Derby Railway. The cost was £17,625 and the contractors were MacGregor and Howe. The track is carried about

23ft high on nineteen arches, all of 30ft span except the southernmost which has to cross the Glascote road at a skew and is therefore of 60ft span. A corbelled cornice and rusticated masonry are the main concessions to architecture.

Tenders for construction were being invited in May 1837, and the keystone of the last arch was laid on 6 February 1839.

TEDDESLEY HAY

Farm waterwheel (SJ 951161). Teddesley Hall, seat of the Littleton family, is demolished, but the Home Farm survives. Among the brick outbuildings an unpretentious extension contains a waterwheel larger in diameter than any other in Staffordshire. It is also typical of a farm wheel intended solely for private use. As common in such wheels, the drive is not from the shaft but from a toothed ring on the side of the rim, thus allowing a less rigid form of construction.

The wheel, entirely iron, is overshot, 38ft × 2ft 8in wide, and with thirteen arms with a brace between each. The whole wheel is below ground level and, despite the existence of three platforms, narrowness of the pit makes examination difficult. Through an outside door, south of the wheel, may be seen the governor and two hand-wheels for controlling the hatch.

The Hatherton estate ledgers show the wheel was designed to drive primarily a threshing-machine and secondarily a saw-mill, a kibbling-machine and a cutting machine. Made by James Bate of Himley, it was part of an installation of about 1838 and cost £764.

TRYSULL

Mill (SO 851944). Trysull Mill used water power until 1940. A 17ft 6in × 6ft 2in level-breast wheel, entirely of iron and with eight arms survives, also the gearing and the three pairs of stones. The mill dated '1854' belonged to Lord Wrottesley, which explains the attention to design reflected in the choice of blue bricks for quoins and buttresses. The waterwheel is signed on the shroud by George Turton of Kidderminster who flourished when the mill was built.

TUTBURY

Mill (SK 287223). Tutbury Mill, if identifiable with a mill in the manor of Rolleston, is in the Domesday Survey; it is two storeys high, and of brick. The two waterwheels are the only water-driven machinery to remain. Placed abreast, both are undershot and iron apart from wooden arms and floats. The northern wheel, 15ft 8in × 5ft 2in, has two sets of eight arms; the southern wheel, 14ft 9in × 5ft, has two sets of six arms. There are signs of the three pairs of stones formerly driven by the northern wheel. Since 1915 the mill has tanned and dressed skins.

Glassworks (SK 212288). In 1834 it was said that the 'steam-mill, employed in cutting glass, commenced about twenty years ago'. Two furnaces existing in 1880, one with ten pots and the other with eight, have been removed and replaced by gas-fired furnaces; but a stone from the northern one has been reset in the wall of the process room; it bears the initials of Henry Jackson, glass-cutter, and the date '1836'.

UTTOXETER RURAL

Mill (SK 044311). The wheelhouse of Burndhurst Mill was removed in 1963, leaving open to view an undershot wheel, 10ft 11in × 4ft 8in. Of cast iron, it has six arms and wooden floats, added for appearance's sake in place of the original twenty-four buckets. The wallower inside the mill is signed underneath by C. Kirk of Etruria. There were four pairs of stones, three burrs and one peak, and all but one runner remain in position.

WALSALL

Drop-forge (SO 981967). The passageway between Nos 98 and 100 Walsall Road, King's Hill, Wednesbury, looks like any other in a terrace of nineteenth-century cottages, but is exceptional for it still leads to a small industrial works. Henry and Frank Robinson are drop-forgers, following the traditional methods of their father and

N

grandfather, and their premises, roofed with corrugated sheeting and partly dry-walled with brick, typify the unpretentious character formerly possessed by most such buildings in the Black Country. The main workshop contains a coke-fired hearth and three drop-stamps. Power is supplied by an electric dynamo which replaced a gas-engine, but in a side building two olivers, each served by its own hearth, are still foot-operated.

Mill (SP 005987). Bearing inscription 'ALBION FLOUR MILL ERECTED A.D. 1849', this four-storey building with three rows of four cast-iron columns and semicircular-headed windows belongs to the most impressive steam-powered complex of its kind in Staffordshire. The machinery is largely by Henry Simon Ltd of Manchester and Cheadle Heath. The smaller matching building on the other side of Canal Street, used for wheat preparation, rises above a conveniently-sited canal basin, and the two are joined by a later bridge.

WATERHOUSES

Mill (SK 062511). In 1827 there was an iron forge and a flax mill, 64ft long × 24ft wide, at Winkhill; these dimensions correspond with those of the present stone and tiled building. The earliest part is the east end, 17ft long; the main range was built next, producing a continuous two-storey mill, and finally the west end received a three-storey addition, now derelict and 38ft wide. The dam that formed a 2 acre pond remains, but nothing is left of the three waterwheels.

WEDNESBURY, see WALSALL.

WEST BROMWICH

Canal bridge (SO 950926). The curving course of the canal between Birmingham and Wolverhampton, the shortness of its summit and the number of locks were so inconvenient that the Birmingham Canal Company in 1824 invited Thomas Telford to make a survey. He recommended construction of a new canal from Smethwick to Tipton at a level of 453ft. At Tipton the new canal was to rise by three locks and, for a short length, join the original canal completed in 1772, the junction being just short of Factory Bridge.

Rebuilding Factory Bridge carrying the Tipton–Wednesbury road was part of Telford's improvement of Brindley's Birmingham Canal. The new structure was iron apart from abutments mainly of brick. The deck was supported by two pairs of spandrel-shaped ribs boldly inscribed 'FACTORY BRIDGE ERECTED MDCCCXXV'. The soffit of the arch was formed of plates resting on eight ribs, and a decorative pattern enlivened the openwork parapet. The bridge was removed in 1970 but parts are to be re-erected at the Black Country Museum at the Tipton end of Dudley Canal Tunnel (p 163).

WETTON

Copper and lead mines (SJ 0958). At Ecton Hill some ladders and tramway sleepers have survived underground, and on the surface noteworthy sites include:

Dutchman Mine: The buried entrance to Dutchman Level is identified by the massive spoil-heap (098582) that overshadows Ecton village.

Ecton Engine House (098583): The two-storey stone and tiled building contained the Boulton & Watt steam engine of 1788. Its stack remains but has been reduced to about 10ft. The site of a gin-race lies to the north.

Ecton Deep Adit: Was driven under the superintendence of Robert Shore in 1774. The inscription '1774 RS', over the well-constructed entrance (096581) is not original.

WIGGINTON

Pumping station (SK 172049). Plans for a pumping station at Hopwas to supply Tamworth with water were prepared by 'Mr. Marten'; by July 1881 the pumps, designed to raise about ½ million gal per day, were in operation. The red-brick gabled engine house is entered through a pedimented doorcase beneath a venetian window.

Inside, the pair of beam steam-engines by Gimson & Co of Leicester remain although superseded by electric pumps. Of 5ft stroke and 25in bore they incorporate such refinements as adjustable cut-off to the steam slide valves. They ran at 17rpm at a pressure of 35lb per square inch. The two mahogany-lagged cylinders bear the names *Spruce* and *Woody* as a tribute to two members of the Tamworth Waterworks Board.

WINKHILL, see WATERHOUSES

WOLVERHAMPTON

Brewery (SO 919993). The original Springfield Brewery erected by William Butler lies at the south-west angle of the triangular site. Crowned by a clock-turret it bears a tablet inscribed 'SPRINGFIELD BREWERY 1873' on the west side. The second brewery, completed 1881, lies to the east and is four storeys high. As late as about 1890 the two breweries were worked independently up to the cooling process, now they are merged. The 1881 brewery contains six mash-tuns bearing dates from 1890 to 1899; the 1873 brewery has been enlarged and is notable for the retention of eight fermenting rounds each with a capacity of 160 barrels.

North and west of the yard two malthouses are now bottling stores and case stores and, on the east, stables for sixty horses are now a dining-room and canteen. The apex of the site is filled by the cooperage where wooden casks are repaired but no longer made.

WOMBOURNE

Mill (SO 858923). The site of a forge in the seventeenth and eighteenth centuries, the present red-brick slated Heath Mill evidently ground corn. Its southern elavation bears the date '1827' and the initials of Sir John Wrottesley. An extension at the end of the original mill contains the overshot waterwheel made entirely of iron; it has two sets of eight arms and is 18ft 4in diameter × 6ft 3in wide.

Mill (SO 885935). At Wodehouse Mill the iron overshot waterwheel, 17ft × 3ft 5in, has two sets of eight arms, and is inscribed on the shroud 'G. & R. TURTON KIDD^R. 1840'. It still runs daily except Sundays for grinding corn into meal.

Canal locks (SO 867938). The three locks at Bratch on the Staffordshire & Worcestershire Canal are unique in being an embryo form of staircase. Instead of a direct progression, the locks are separated by extremely short pounds not even large enough to take a boat or all the discharged water from a lock. As a result, there are peculiarities of construction and operation. A weir above the top lock takes the overflow into a pair of side ponds, which receive overflow from the short pound below the top lock and from the short pound below the middle lock respectively. The short pounds are connected to the side ponds by culverts, and in operating the locks the top gates must be closed when emptying the lock above, otherwise the gates will obstruct the mouth of the culvert and the lower lock will be flooded. An overflow at top water-level of the bottom lock reduces the effect of this calamity. Conversely, when the middle and bottom locks are being filled, water from the side ponds is required to make up for the deficiency of the short pounds.

At such a complex and unusual series of locks, a lock-keeper is especially needed. He occupies the two-storey house beside the top lock. Between this lock and the middle one, Upper Bratch Bridge takes the towpath over the canal, and on the east stands an octagonal tollhouse with stone chimney-like finial. Bratch Bridge takes a road over the canal below the bottom lock, and here there is a fascinating pattern of steps (to allow access to the canal-side) and of parapets and an arch (to prevent fouling of the tow-rope and slipping accidents).

Pumping station (SO 868937). The object overlooking the Bratch Canal locks is not a Scottish baronial castle but a pumping station opened on 12 August 1897. Designed by Baldwin Latham of Westminster, the waterworks are red Ruabon brick with blue-brick bands, with a stepped pattern of red, buff and blue bricks decorating the panels above and between the windows. Four entirely non-functional bartizans rise from the corners of the engine house which is entered through a multi-coloured Gothic doorway beneath a stone tablet inscribed 'BILSTON WATER WORKS 1895'. The two triple-expansion steam engines, by Thornewill & Warham of Burton-upon-Trent, date from 1897 and until stopped in 1960 could pump 1 million gal in 20hr. In recognition of the Diamond Jubilee they are named *Victoria* and *Alexandra*. Each is of 4ft stroke, and the cylinder diameters are 16in (HP), 26in (IP), and 40in (LP). The pump house is connected to the engine house by a Gothic arch, and three boilers were contained in the boiler houses to the west.

YOXALL

Mill (SK 138209). Wood Mill is a brick extension to a timber-framed building. Although no longer in use the contents are largely intact. The overshot wheel, 14ft × 3ft 8in, has six wooden arms and wooden sole-boards, buckets and shaft. Feed is from a stream that, when not driving the mill, passes through two sluice gates and over an imposing weir to the east.

Bibliography

THE following contains the main sources that have been used. Works not specifically relating to Staffordshire and sources cited in the text and in captions to diagrams in text are generally not included. The abbreviation SRO stands for Staffordshire Record Office.

GENERAL

Boulton & Watt Collection, 'Engine Book' and drawings, Birmingham Reference Library

Com Employment of Children, 2nd report (1843), Parliamentary Reports vols 14–15, Command 431–2

Crompton, W. H., Map of Lichfield (1862)

Lichfield Joint Record Office, Tithe Maps and Apportionment Awards

Malabar, R., Map of Newcastle-under-Lyme (1847 and c1861)

Map of Leek (1838)

Meredith, W. D., 'Watermills in North Staffordshire', *North Staffs Journal of Field Studies*, vol 4 (1964)

Newcastle-under-Lyme and Stoke-on-Trent, Victoria County History of Staffs, vol 8

Plot, R., *Natural History of Staffordshire* (Oxford, 1686), containing descriptions of communications and techniques

Sherlock, R. J., 'Industrial Archaeology', *North Staffs Journal of Field Studies*, vol 2 (1962)

Slagg, C., Map of Leek (1862)

Smith, D. M., 'Industrial Archaeology in Potteries', *North Staffs Journal of Field Studies*, vol 5 (1965)

Spooner, T., Map of Burton-upon-Trent (1865)

Staffordshire Advertiser, from 1795, containing advertisements of sales and reports of events, eg meetings, disasters, openings of railways

Staffordshire Census, 1851: Public Record Office (London) HO 107

Staffordshire CC Education Department Source Books, Roads (1968)

——, Coal Mines (1968)

——, Pottery Industry (1969)

——, Waterways (1969)

——, Railways (1971)

——, Textile Industries (1971)

Staffordshire Industries, Victoria County History of Staffordshire, vol 2

SRO, Map of Stone, D1185 (1880)

——, Q/R/Pl, Land Tax Returns

Sun Fire Office Registers, Guildhall Library, MSS 11,936–7, by courtesy of Sun Alliance & London Insurance Group

White, *Directory of Staffordshire* (1834 and 1851)

Wood, J., Map of Stafford (1835)

GLASS, POTTERY AND LEATHER

Beaver, S. H., 'The Potteries: A study in the Evolution of a Cultural Landscape', *Trans Inst Brit Geographers*, no 34 (1964)

Buckley, F., 'Notes on the Glasshouses of Stourbridge 1700–1830', *Trans Soc Glass Technology*, vol 11 (1927)

Copeland, R., 'Cheddleton Flint Mill', *North Staffs Journal of Field Studies*, vol 9 (1969)

Crossley, D. W., 'Glassmaking in Bagot's Park,' *Post-Medieval Archaeology*, vol 1 (1967)

Graham, M., *Cup and Saucer Land* (c1905)

Guttery, D. R., *From Broad-Glass to Cut Crystal* (1956)

Haden, H. J., *Notes on the Stourbridge Glass Trade* (Brierley Hill, 1949)

Knight, C., et al, *The Land We Live In*, vol 4 (1850)

Pape, T., 'An Elizabethan Glass Furnace', *The Connoisseur* (Sept 1933)
Shaw, S., *History of the Staffordshire Potteries* (Hanley, 1829)

TEXTILES

Deeds of No 14 King Street, Leek; No 1 Pickwood Road, Leek; and
  Court No 2 Wood Street, Leek (in private possession)
SRO, D624 (Tutbury Mill, Rocester)
——, D644 (Property of J. & N. Philips)
——, D1040/1/1 (Leek township church rate)

MALTING AND BREWING

Barnard, A., *Noted Breweries of Great Britain and Ireland* (1889–91),
  containing descriptions of breweries at Burton-upon-Trent,
  Lichfield, Stone and Wolverhampton
Molyneux, W., *Burton-on-Trent* (1869)
Plans of Bass & Co's premises, 1859 and 1862 (in private possession)
Railway Magazine, vols 57–8, Feb 1926, 'A Notable Brewery Railway
  System'
SRO, D206/M/3–4 (Shelton Brewery)
——, D901/1 (Bond End malthouse, Yoxall)

COAL, IRON AND OTHER MINERAL RESOURCES

Gale, W. K. V., 'Notes on the Black Country Iron Trade', *Trans
  Newcomen Soc*, vol 24 (1949)
Gale, W. K. V., *Black Country Iron Industry* (1966)
Jones, J. I., 'Licensed Coalmining in North Staffordshire', *North
  Staffs Journal of Field Studies*, vol 9 (1969)
Jukes, J. Beete, 'Geology of the South Staffordshire Coal Field' etc,
  Records of School of Mines, vol 1, part 2, with chapter by Waring-
  ton Smyth, pp 339 ff
Morton, G. R., 'Paget Ironworks', *Trans South Staffs Arch & Hist
  Soc*, vol 6 (1964–5)

Morton, G. R., and Gould, J., 'Little Aston Forge: 1574–1798', *Journal Iron & Steel Institute*, vol 205 (1967)

Morton, G. R., and Le Guillou, M., 'Rise and Fall of the South Staffordshire Pig Iron Industry', *The British Foundryman* (July 1967)

Morton, G. R., and Smith, W. A., 'Bradley Ironworks of John Wilkinson', *Journal Iron & Steel Institute*, vol 204 (July 1966)

Moseley, A. F., 'The Nailmakers', *Journal West Midlands Regional Studies*, vol 2 (1968)

Robey, J. A., and Porter, L., *Copper & Lead Mines of Ecton Hill* (Cheddleton and Bakewell, 1972), citing other sources

ROADS

Burne, S. A. H., 'Coaching Age in Staffordshire', *Trans North Staffs Field Club*, vol 56 (1921–2)

Dodd, A. E. and E. M., 'Old Road from Ashbourne to Leek', *Trans North Staffs Field Club*, vol 83–4 (1948–9 and (1949–50)

Dodd, E. M., 'Blythe Marsh to Thorpe Turnpike, *North Staffs Journal of Field Studies*, vol 5 (1965)

SRO, D239/M/Boxes 3–16 (Cheadle Turnpike Trust)

Thomas, Annie Longton, 'North Staffordshire Transport and Communications in 18th century', *Staffs Hist. Collection*, part 1 (1934)

CANALS

Dodd, A. E. and E. M., 'Froghall–Uttoxeter Canal', *North Staffs Journal of Field Studies*, vol 3 (1963)

Gibson, C. J., 'Wyrley & Essington Canal', *Trans South Staffs Arch & Hist Soc*, vol 1 (1959–60)

Hollick, J. R., 'Caldon Low Tramways', *Railway Magazine*, vol 80 (June 1937)

RAILWAYS

British Transport Historical Records, minutes North Staffordshire Railway

Clinker, C. R., *Railways of the West Midlands: A Chronology* (1954)
MacDermot, E. T., *History of the Great Western Railway* (1964)
'Manifold', *North Staffordshire Railway* (Ashbourne, 1952)
'Manifold', *Leek & Manifold Valley Light Railway* (Ashbourne, 1955)
SRO, D615/E(L)/14/1, contract between Earl of Lichfield and Trent Valley Railway Co, containing references to Shugborough Railway Bridge and Tunnel

Index